WeightWatchers

FABULOUS & *filling*

SIMON & SCHUSTER
A CBS COMPANY

Tamsin Burnett-Hall

First published in Great Britain by Simon & Schuster UK Ltd, 2010
A CBS Company

Simon & Schuster UK Ltd, 1st Floor, 222 Gray's Inn Road,
London WC1X 8HB

13579108642

Weight Watchers Publications Team: Jane Griffiths, Nina McKerlie and Fiona Smith
Simon & Schuster Project Editor: Anna Hitchin
Photography by Steve Baxter
Styling by Rachel Jukes
Food preparation and styling by Penny Stephens
Design and typesetting by Jane Humphrey

Printed and bound in China

A CIP catalogue for this book is available from the British Library

Pictured on the front cover: Rosemary Roast Chicken, page 102

Pictured on the back cover from left to right: Sweetcorn Fritters with Spicy Tomatoes, page 16; Teriyaki Beef Udon, page 68; Spinach, Mushroom and Chestnut Torte, page 88; Fig and Raspberry Clafoutis, page 172

Pictured on the inside front flap: Hot Chocolate Pudding, page 174

Pictured on the contents page, from left to right: Sunshine Breakfast Egg, page 18; Mediterranean Vegetable Soup, page 24; Tandoori Lamb Kebabs with Minted Rice, page 72; Lemon and Passion Fruit Drizzle Cake, page 182.

Pictured on page 4: Cheese and Tomato Bread Pudding, page 108

POINTS® value logo: You'll find this easy to read ***POINTS*** value logo on every recipe throughout this book. The logo represents the number of ***POINTS*** values per serving each recipe contains. Weight Watchers ***POINTS*** Weight Loss System is a simple way to lose weight. As part of the Weight Watchers **Discover Plan™** you'll enjoy eating delicious, healthy, filling foods that help to keep you feeling satisfied for longer and in control of both your portion sizes and your hunger.

Filling Foods are highlighted in green – like this. Focus on these foods where you can – they keep you feeling satisfied for longer.

This symbol denotes a vegetarian recipe and assumes that, where relevant, free range eggs, vegetarian cheese, vegetarian virtually fat free fromage frais, vegetarian low fat crème fraîche and vegetarian low fat yogurts are used. Virtually fat free fromage frais, low fat crème fraîche and low fat yogurts may contain traces of gelatine so they are not always vegetarian. Please check the labels.

This symbol denotes a dish that can be frozen.

Recipe notes

Egg size Medium, unless otherwise stated.
All fruits and vegetables Medium size unless otherwise stated.
Raw eggs Only the freshest eggs should be used. Pregnant women, the elderly and children should avoid recipes with eggs which are not fully cooked or raw.
Recipe timings These are approximate and meant to be guidelines. Please note that the preparation time includes all the steps up to and following the main cooking time(s).
Low fat spread Where a recipe states to use a low fat spread, a light spread with a fat content of no less than 38% should be used.
Stock Stock cubes should be used in the recipes, unless otherwise stated. Prepare them according to the packet instructions.

Contents

Welcome to Weight Watchers and the new **Discover Plan** cookbook, *Fabulous & Filling*. Our aim is not just to help you lose weight but to help you keep it off for the long haul. Because what you choose to eat is an important part of that success, the **Discover Plan** helps you to make informed, satisfying choices and **keep hunger at bay**.

With new *Fabulous & Filling* you'll find making meal choices easier than ever. There are 125 new and satisfying recipes to try, many of which contain **Filling Foods** that can help to S-T-R-E-T-C-H your ***POINTS*** values so you can eat more and make your daily allowance go further. **Filling Foods** can help you to stay satisfied for longer.

Fabulous & Filling is full of simple to follow recipes that are easy to make and ideal for today's busy lifestyles. And to make it easier to stay on track with your ***POINTS*** allowance, the ***POINTS*** values per serving are clearly shown on every recipe.

There's something for everyone and whether you're looking for a new and exciting breakfast, a zero ***POINTS*** value soup for lunch or a quick and easy dinner, **you'll be spoilt for choice**. Enjoy a fantastic selection of family favourites as well as midweek meals, all ready in 30 minutes or less. Look out for the vegetarian chapter with delicious and original recipes, packed full of **Filling Foods**. A whole chapter is devoted to comforting meals and another has a fantastic selection of recipes for special occasions. To **treat yourself**, turn to the chapter packed with delicious bakes and desserts. And for when you haven't got a whole household to cook for, there's a chapter for cooking for one.

We hope you enjoy *Fabulous & Filling* as you discover the satisfaction of creating delicious, healthy meals for yourself, your family and your friends while still keeping your weight loss on track.

chapter

1 Breakfast

Start your day feeling **satisfied and energised** with these quick and delicious breakfast ideas. If you're short on time, a Peach and Mango Smoothie can be whizzed up in a matter of minutes. And when the weekend arrives, you can slow down and savour the One Dish Baked Breakfast or Sweetcorn Fritters with Spicy Tomatoes.

Sunshine breakfast egg on page 18

Cinnamon and sultana porridge

Oats are an excellent way to start the day as they provide slow release energy to keep you going all morning.

Serves 1 | **Takes 8** minutes | **4 *POINTS*** values per recipe | **282** calories per serving

40 g (1½ oz) **porridge oats**
a pinch of salt
a pinch of ground cinnamon
15 g (½ oz) sultanas
150 ml (5 fl oz) **skimmed milk**
2 teaspoons golden syrup or maple syrup, to serve

Method

1 Place the oats, salt, cinnamon, sultanas and milk in a saucepan with 100 ml (3½ fl oz) water.
2 Bring to the boil, stirring occasionally, and cook for 4–5 minutes until thickened.
3 Serve with the syrup drizzled over the porridge.

Apricot and yogurt crunch

The crunchy granola-style topping can be made in a larger quantity and stored in an airtight container once cooled, ready for a speedy start in the morning.

Serves 2 | **Takes 15** minutes | **6 *POINTS*** values per recipe | **231** calories per serving

low fat cooking spray
25 g (1 oz) **porridge oats**
1 tablespoon sunflower seeds
2 heaped teaspoons clear honey, warmed
200 g pot **low fat vanilla yogurt**
210 g can **apricots in natural juice**, *drained and sliced*

Method

1 Preheat the oven to Gas Mark 5/190°C/fan oven 170°C. Spray a baking tray with low fat cooking spray. Mix the oats, sunflower seeds and honey together and spread out on the baking tray. Toast in the oven for 6–8 minutes until golden brown, stirring halfway through.
2 Leave to cool on the tray for 2–3 minutes, during which time the oat mixture will become crunchy.
3 Layer up the yogurt and apricots in two glasses or bowls and then top with the crunchy oat and seed mixture just before eating.

Why not try... varying the fruit according to the season. In summer, replace the tinned apricots with 150 g (5½ oz) sliced strawberries or raspberries for the same ***POINTS*** values per serving.

3
POINTS
VALUE

Banana power bars

3½ *POINTS* value

Make these energy packed bars at the weekend and pop them in the freezer – that way you'll have an instant breakfast to grab on weekday mornings. Enjoy with an apple on the side, for an extra ½ *POINTS* value per serving.

Makes 10 | **Takes 10** minutes to prepare, **20–25** minutes to cook | **33 *POINTS*** values per recipe | **211** calories per serving

100 g (3½ oz) low fat spread
50 g (1¾ oz) golden syrup
50 g (1¾ oz) demerara sugar
100 g (3½ oz) self raising flour
a pinch of salt
125 g (4½ oz) **porridge oats**
40 g (1½ oz) dried cranberries
25 g (1 oz) pumpkin seeds
2 ripe **bananas**, *mashed*
1 **egg**, *beaten*

Method

1 Preheat the oven to Gas Mark 4/180°C/fan oven 160°C. Line and grease a baking tin measuring approximately 17 x 25 cm (6½ x 10 inches).
2 Gently heat the low fat spread, syrup and sugar together in a saucepan until melted, then set aside to cool slightly.
3 Sift the flour and salt into a bowl and then stir in the oats, cranberries and pumpkin seeds. Mix the mashed bananas and egg together and stir into the oats, followed by the syrup mixture.
4 Pour into the prepared tin then bake in the oven for 20–25 minutes until golden brown and firm to the touch.
5 Cool in the tin and then cut into 10 bars.

Peach and mango smoothie

This exotic-tasting smoothie will set you up nicely in the morning. A smoothie is a filling breakfast choice because it contains all the fibre of the whole fruit which has simply been puréed.

Serves 2 | **Takes 5** minutes | **4 *POINTS*** values per recipe | **143** calories per serving

411 g can **peach slices in natural juice**
1 ripe **mango**, *peeled and stoned*
juice of a lime
4 ice cubes

Method

1 Tip the peaches and their juice into the jug of a liquidiser or a similar container if you have a hand held blender.
2 Roughly chop the mango flesh and add to the jug or container, along with the lime juice and ice cubes.
3 Blend until smooth and serve immediately.

Cook's tip... Use a swivel-bladed vegetable peeler to easily remove the peel from the mango, then slice the flesh away from the large flat central stone.

2
POINTS
VALUE

One dish baked breakfast

This all in one cooked breakfast is very easy to prepare, and keeps your kitchen smelling lovely and fresh as it's baked in the oven rather than cooked on the hob.

Serves 4 | **Takes 5** minutes to prepare, **20** minutes to cook | **12 *POINTS*** values per recipe | **222** calories per serving

low fat cooking spray
3 medium slices bread
3 teaspoons low fat spread
4 **turkey rashers***, snipped roughly*
100 g (3½ oz) **mushrooms***, quartered*
150 g (5½ oz) **cherry tomatoes***, halved*
4 **eggs**
150 ml (5 fl oz) skimmed milk
salt and freshly ground black pepper

Method

1 Preheat the oven to Gas Mark 5/190°C/fan oven 170°C. Lightly spray a 23 cm (9 inch) square baking dish with the cooking spray.

2 Spread the bread thinly with the low fat spread, then cut each slice into four triangles and arrange around the edge of the dish, points uppermost. Scatter the turkey rashers, mushrooms and cherry tomatoes in the centre of the dish.

3 Beat the eggs and milk with seasoning then pour all over the other ingredients. Bake in the oven for 20 minutes until the egg mixture is set, and the bread is crisp and toasted.

Scrambled egg and smoked salmon muffin

4½ POINTS VALUE (9)

This fabulous cooked breakfast with a touch of luxury is ready in just 5 minutes. The sandwich sized slices of smoked salmon found in supermarkets are perfect for this recipe – you will need two slices.

Serves 1 | **Takes 5** minutes | **4½ *POINTS*** values per recipe | **281** calories per serving

1 wholemeal English muffin, halved
1 **egg**
1 tablespoon **skimmed milk**
2 teaspoons snipped fresh **chives**
low fat cooking spray
30 g (1¼ oz) **smoked salmon**
freshly ground black pepper

Method

1 Lightly toast the muffin and keep warm.

2 Meanwhile, beat the egg with the milk and black pepper, then mix in the chives. Spray a non stick saucepan with the cooking spray and quickly cook the egg mixture, stirring until softly set.

3 Top the muffin halves with the smoked salmon and spoon the scrambled eggs on top. Eat straightaway.

Why not try... 30 g (1¼ oz) cooked ham instead of smoked salmon, for the same ***POINTS*** values per serving.

4 1/2
POINTS
VALUE

Potato cakes with ham and eggs

(7) 3½ POINTS VALUE

These Irish potato cakes can also be made with 250 g (9 oz) leftover mashed potato, for the same *POINTS* values and it will cut down the preparation time too. Enjoy with 250 ml (9 fl oz) of orange juice, for an additional 1½ *POINTS* values per serving.

❄ Potato cakes only | **Serves 4** | **Takes 35** minutes | **14½ *POINTS*** values per recipe | **241** calories per serving

300 g (10½ oz) potatoes*, peeled and diced*
1 teaspoon low fat spread
60 g (2 oz) plain flour plus 1 tablespoon for rolling
a pinch of salt
¼ teaspoon baking powder
low fat cooking spray
freshly ground black pepper

To serve
4 **eggs**
125 g (4½ oz) **wafer thin smoked ham**

Method

1 Bring a lidded pan of water to the boil and drop in the diced potatoes. Cover and cook for 12 minutes or until tender. Drain well and then return to the pan and leave to steam dry over a low heat for 1 minute. Mash with the low fat spread and black pepper, then sift the flour minus the reserved tablespoon for rolling, together with the salt and baking powder. Mix well with a wooden spoon until you have a soft, smooth dough.

2 Flour the work surface with the remaining flour. Tip the dough out and divide into two balls. Roll each one out to a circle about 18 cm (7 inches) in diameter and cut into quarters.

3 Heat a non stick frying pan until hot and spray with the cooking spray. Add four potato cake quarters to the pan and cook for around 3 minutes on each side over a medium heat until golden brown and crisp. Keep warm while you cook the remaining potato cakes.

4 While the potato cakes are cooking, bring a large pan of water to the boil for the poached eggs. Break an egg into each of two ramekins or cups and then slide the egg into the boiling water on opposite sides of the pan. Immediately reduce the heat to a gentle simmer, and then add the other two eggs in the same manner. Cook for 3 minutes, or until the eggs are cooked to your liking, then lift out using a draining spoon.

5 Serve two potato cakes per person, topped with a quarter of the wafer thin ham and a poached egg.

3 1/2
POINTS
VALUE

Sweetcorn fritters with spicy tomatoes

Give tomatoes some kick with a little Tabasco sauce and see how scrumptious they are with sweetcorn fritters.

Serves 4 (makes 12) | **Takes 20** minutes | **12½ *POINTS*** values per recipe | **247** calories per serving

250 g (9 oz) frozen or tinned **sweetcorn**
150 g (5½ oz) self raising flour
a pinch of salt
1 **egg**
175 ml (6 fl oz) **skimmed milk**
low fat cooking spray
400 g can **cherry tomatoes**
2 tablespoons tomato ketchup
a few shakes of Tabasco
freshly ground black pepper

Method

1 If using frozen sweetcorn, place it in a bowl, cover with boiling water for two minutes then drain. If using tinned sweetcorn, drain.

2 Sift the flour and salt into a mixing bowl, season with black pepper and then whisk in the egg and milk to give a smooth batter. Stir in the sweetcorn.

3 Heat a non stick frying pan to a medium heat and then spray with the cooking spray. Drop four separate tablespoonfuls of the sweetcorn batter into the frying pan and cook for 2–3 minutes on each side until golden brown and cooked through. Keep warm while you cook the remaining batter to give a total of 12 fritters.

4 Meanwhile, place the cherry tomatoes and their juice in a pan with the ketchup and a couple of shakes of Tabasco, according to taste. Simmer gently for about 5 minutes, then serve as a sauce with the sweetcorn fritters. Serve three fritters per person.

Cook's tip... Tabasco is quite fiery so add it a drop at a time, to taste.

Smart ideas...

Eating a filling and balanced breakfast can give you a great start so you don't begin to feel hungry by mid-morning.

3
POINTS
VALUE

Sunshine breakfast egg

A cheerful and quick cooked breakfast that looks as good as it tastes.

Serves 1 | **Takes 10** minutes | **3** ***POINTS*** values per recipe | **229** calories per serving

1 medium slice of bread
1 teaspoon low fat spread
1 large flat **mushroom**
1 **tomato**, *halved*
low fat cooking spray
1 **egg**

Method

1 Preheat the grill to medium. Lightly spread the bread with low fat spread on both sides. Use an 8 cm (3¼ inch) cutter to stamp out a disc from the slice of bread, but don't remove the bread disc from the centre of the slice yet. Heat a lidded non stick frying pan.

2 Place the mushroom and tomato halves on the grill pan and spray with the cooking spray. Grill for 6–7 minutes, turning over the mushroom halfway through the cooking time.

3 Meanwhile, spray the frying pan with the cooking spray. Separate the disc from the bread slice and add both to the pan. Fry for 3 minutes over a medium heat until the bread is crisp and golden on the bottom.

4 Flip both pieces of bread and then break the egg into the hole in the slice of bread. Cover the pan and cook gently for 3 minutes, or until the egg is cooked to your liking.

5 Serve the toasted bread and egg on a warmed plate with the mushroom on top of the toasted bread circle and the grilled tomatoes.

Sausage and potato sauté

This is a great weekend breakfast dish. It's also good topped with a poached egg, for an extra 1½ ***POINTS*** **values per serving, or served with grilled tomatoes for no additional** ***POINTS*** **values.**

Serves 2 | **Takes 20** minutes | **5½** ***POINTS*** values per recipe | **224** calories per serving

low fat cooking spray
250 g (9 oz) **potatoes**, *cut into 2 cm (¾ inch) dice*
½ **onion**, *chopped roughly*
1 **pepper** *(any colour), de-seeded and chopped roughly*
3 Quorn sausages, sliced thickly

Method

1 Heat a lidded, non stick frying pan until hot and spray with the cooking spray. Fry the potatoes for 3 minutes over a high heat until starting to brown.

2 Reduce the heat to medium, add 2 tablespoons of water and cook, covered, for 3 minutes.

3 Stir in the onion, pepper and sausages. Then cover the pan again and fry for a further 10 minutes, stirring occasionally until the vegetables are tender and everything is nicely browned. If necessary, add a splash of water to stop the sautéed ingredients from sticking to the pan and burning. Serve immediately.

Why not try... using three low fat pork sausages rather than Quorn sausages, for 2½ ***POINTS*** values per person. Instead of slicing the pork sausages, use kitchen scissors to snip them into pieces – it's much easier.

3
POINTS
VALUE

Apple and raspberry muffins

Enjoy this deliciously moist muffin with a skinny latte, made with a ½ pint (300 ml) of skimmed milk, for an extra 1 *POINTS* value per serving.

Makes 12 | **Takes 10** minutes to prepare, **20** minutes to cook | **30½ *POINTS*** values per recipe | **162** calories per serving

low fat cooking spray
225 g (8 oz) self raising flour
1 teaspoon bicarbonate of soda
a pinch of salt
25 g (1 oz) **porridge oats**
100 g (3½ oz) caster sugar
150 g (5½ oz) **apple sauce**
3 tablespoons sunflower oil
175 g (6 oz) **low fat natural yogurt**
6 tablespoons **skimmed milk**
1 **egg**, *beaten*
100 g (3½ oz) **raspberries**, *fresh or frozen*

Method

1 Preheat the oven to Gas Mark 6/200°C/fan oven 180°C. Lightly grease a non stick 12 hole muffin tin with the cooking spray or simply use 12 paper cases and place in the holes in the tin.

2 Sift the flour, bicarbonate of soda and salt into a mixing bowl. Reserve 1 tablespoon of oats for the muffin tops, then stir the remaining oats and sugar into the flour.

3 In a separate bowl, mix the apple sauce, oil, yogurt, milk and egg together, then stir this wet mixture into the dry ingredients, mixing until just combined but still slightly lumpy. Stir in the raspberries, then spoon into the muffin tins, dividing the mixture evenly to make 12 muffins. Scatter with the reserved oats and bake in the oven for 20 minutes until risen, firm and golden brown.

4 Cool on a wire rack.

Cook's tips... Look out for reusable silicone muffin cases. They are wonderful for baking as you don't need to grease them, yet they'll still easily peel away from your baked muffins.

... Frozen berries can be stirred straight into the batter; there's no need to defrost them first.

Why not try... using 100 g (3½ oz) blueberries instead of raspberries in these muffins, for the same ***POINTS*** values per serving. Add a pinch of ground cinnamon too.

2½
POINTS
VALUE

chapter 2

Lunches and light bites

Give yourself **something scrumptious** to look forward to at work or out and about. Choose from a fantastic selection of new and inspiring ideas for soups, salads and sandwiches to **fill you up** and keep you going all afternoon. Whether you're in the office or on the go, you'll love the Rice Noodle Salad with Prawns or the Lime and Coriander Chicken Bagel.

Curried sweet potato and lentil soup on page 26

Carrot, squash and pepper soup

This satisfyingly thick soup has a pleasing hint of smokiness.

Serves 6 | **Takes 10** minutes to prepare, **20** minutes to cook | **0 *POINTS*** values per recipe | **101** calories per serving

low fat cooking spray
2 red **peppers**, *de-seeded and chopped roughly*
1 **onion**, *chopped roughly*
400 g (14 oz) **carrots**, *peeled and chopped roughly*
750 g (1 lb 10 oz) **butternut squash**, *peeled, de-seeded and chopped roughly*
1 teaspoon smoked paprika
1.5 litres (2¾ pints) hot vegetable stock

Method

1 Spray a large, lidded saucepan with the cooking spray. Fry the peppers and onion for around 4 minutes over a high heat, stirring occasionally, until they start to brown.

2 Add the carrots, butternut squash and paprika, followed by the stock. Bring to the boil, cover and simmer for 20 minutes or until the vegetables are tender.

3 Blend until smooth using a liquidiser, or use a hand held blender. Return to the pan if necessary and heat through. Serve in warm bowls.

Mediterranean vegetable soup

A chunky soup, packed with the flavours of the sun-drenched Mediterranean. A wedge of Rosemary and Olive Soda Bread per person (on page 162) goes well with this soup, for an extra 2 *POINTS* values per serving.

Serves 6 | **Takes 20** minutes | **0 *POINTS*** values per recipe | **54** calories per serving

low fat cooking spray
1 **fennel** *bulb, diced or sliced thinly, or 4* **celery** *sticks, sliced*
3 **carrots**, *peeled and diced*
2 **garlic cloves**, *sliced*
1.2 litres (2 pints) hot vegetable stock
500 g carton **passata**
2 **courgettes**, *diced*
175 g (6 oz) **green beans**, *chopped roughly*
3 heaped tablespoons shredded fresh **basil**, *plus a few leaves to garnish*
freshly ground black pepper

Method

1 Spray a large, lidded saucepan with the cooking spray. Add the fennel or celery, carrot and garlic and fry for 3 minutes, stirring. Add 4 tablespoons of the stock, cover and cook for 2 minutes until the vegetables are starting to soften.

2 Pour in the rest of the stock and the passata. Season with the black pepper and bring to the boil. Add the courgettes, green beans and basil. Simmer uncovered for 10 minutes or until the vegetables are all tender.

3 Ladle into warm bowls and serve garnished with extra basil leaves.

0
POINTS
VALUE

Curried sweet potato and lentil soup

A delicious and delicately spiced soup.

Serves 4 | **Takes 15** minutes to prepare, **15** minutes to cook | **10 *POINTS*** values per recipe | **214** calories per serving

low fat cooking spray
1 onion, chopped finely
1.2 litres (2 pints) hot vegetable stock
1 green chilli, de-seeded and chopped finely
2 teaspoons finely grated root ginger
1 teaspoon ground cumin
1 tablespoon medium curry powder
400 g (14 oz) sweet potatoes, peeled and diced
100 g (3½ oz) red lentils, rinsed
juice of ½ a lime or lemon

To serve
4 tablespoons 0% fat Greek yogurt
4 tablespoons chopped fresh coriander

Method

1 Heat a large, lidded saucepan and spray with the cooking spray. Fry the onion for 1 minute, and then add 2 tablespoons of the stock and cook, stirring for 3–4 minutes.

2 Stir in the chilli, ginger, cumin and curry powder and cook for 1 minute, then mix in the sweet potatoes, lentils and remaining stock. Bring to the boil, cover and simmer for 15 minutes or until the sweet potatoes and lentils are tender.

3 Transfer the soup to a liquidiser, or use a hand held blender, and blend until smooth, adding the lime or lemon juice. Return to the pan and reheat if necessary. Serve topped with the yogurt and coriander.

Courgette, pea and mint soup

This velvety, green soup has a fresh, summery flavour. A Wensleydale and Spring Onion Scone (on page 158) makes a great accompaniment, for 1½ *POINTS* values per serving.

Serves 4 | **Takes 15** minutes to prepare, **15** minutes to cook | **7 *POINTS*** values per recipe | **159** calories per serving

low fat cooking spray
2 leeks, chopped roughly
2 courgettes, diced
700 ml (1¼ pints) hot vegetable stock
400 g (14 oz) potatoes, peeled and diced
300 ml (10 fl oz) skimmed milk
150 g (5½ oz) frozen peas
3 heaped tablespoons chopped fresh mint
juice of ½ a lemon
freshly ground black pepper

Method

1 Spray a large, lidded saucepan with the cooking spray. Add the leeks and cook, stirring, for 3 minutes. Add the courgettes and 4 tablespoons of the stock. Cover and cook for 3 minutes. Mix in the potatoes and the rest of the stock, plus the milk. Bring to the boil and simmer, partially covered, for 12 minutes or until the potatoes are tender.

2 Add the peas and mint to the pan and cook for 2 minutes more. Transfer the soup to a liquidiser, or use a hand held blender, and blend until smooth, adding the lemon juice and black pepper to taste. Return to the pan and reheat if necessary and serve in warm bowls.

2
POINTS
VALUE

Tomato, celery and apple soup

A fragrant soup with a gentle kick of ginger and pleasantly contrasting sweet and sour flavours.

Serves 4 | **Takes 15** minutes to prepare, **25** minutes to cook | **2 *POINTS*** values per recipe | **83** calories per serving

low fat cooking spray
1 ***onion****, chopped roughly*
850 ml (1½ pints) hot vegetable stock
400 g can chopped ***tomatoes***
4 ***celery*** *sticks, chopped roughly*
1 cooking ***apple****, peeled, cored and chopped*
1 tablespoon finely grated root ginger or 1 teaspoon dried ground ginger
25 g (1 oz) light brown soft sugar
freshly ground black pepper

Method

1 Heat a large, lidded saucepan and spray with the cooking spray. Fry the onion for 3 minutes, stirring. Add 4 tablespoons of the stock, cover the pan and cook for 3 minutes until starting to soften.

2 Add the tomatoes, celery, apple, ginger and sugar, plus the rest of the stock. Season with black pepper and bring to the boil. Simmer, covered, for 25 minutes.

3 Transfer the soup to a liquidiser, or use a hand held blender, and blend until smooth. Return to the pan and reheat if necessary. Serve in warm bowls.

French toasties

Somewhere between a Croque Monsieur and eggy bread, these scrumptious toasties are filled with melted cheese and ham. Serve with a zero ***POINTS*** value salad.

Serves 2 | **Takes 10** minutes | **8½ *POINTS*** values per recipe | **280** calories per serving

4 medium slices wholemeal bread
½ teaspoon Dijon mustard (optional)
60 g (2 oz) ***wafer thin smoked ham***
25 g (1 oz) low fat mature cheese, grated finely
1 ***egg****, beaten*
3 tablespoons ***skimmed milk***
low fat cooking spray
salt and freshly ground black pepper

Method

1 Spread two of the slices of bread thinly with mustard, if using. Divide the ham and cheese between these slices and top with the remaining slices of bread. Cut each sandwich into two triangles.

2 Beat the egg and milk together in a shallow bowl and season. Dip the ham and cheese sandwiches in the egg mixture on both sides, until the mixture has all been soaked up.

3 Heat a non stick frying pan until hot and spray with the cooking spray. Add the egg dipped sandwiches and fry for 2 minutes on each side over a medium heat until golden brown and crisp. Serve immediately.

4 1/2
POINTS
VALUE

Salsa beef wrap

This simple wrap is bursting with fabulous flavours.

Serves 1 | **Takes 8** minutes | **5½ *POINTS*** values per recipe | **245** calories per serving

1 medium soft flour tortilla
40 g (1½ oz) **Iceberg lettuce**, *shredded*
50 g (1¾ oz) thinly sliced cooked **roast beef**
15 g (½ oz) low fat mature cheese, grated

For the salsa
1 small **tomato**, *diced*
1 **spring onion**, *chopped finely*
1 tablespoon chopped fresh **coriander**
a squeeze of lime juice
a few drops of Tabasco

Method

1 Make the salsa by mixing the tomato, spring onion and coriander together with the lime juice and a couple of drops of Tabasco to taste.

2 Warm the tortilla for a few seconds on either side in a non stick frying pan, to make it more flexible. Spoon on the salsa and add the lettuce, roast beef and cheese. Roll up, folding in the ends to enclose the filling and cut in half to serve.

Lime and coriander chicken bagel

If you want to use up a little leftover roast chicken, this appetizing bagel is a great way to do it.

Serves 1 | **Takes 5** minutes | **5½ *POINTS*** values per recipe | **326** calories per serving

1 plain bagel, halved
30 g (1¼ oz) **low fat soft cheese**
finely grated zest of ½ a lime
1 tablespoon chopped fresh **coriander**
60 g (2 oz) cooked **chicken**, *sliced*
15 g (½ oz) baby **salad leaves**
freshly ground black pepper

Method

1 Heat the grill to a medium heat and then lightly toast the bagel on the cut sides.

2 Mix the soft cheese with the lime zest, coriander and black pepper. Spread on both halves of the toasted bagel.

3 Pile the chicken and salad leaves on to the bottom half of the bagel and top with the other half to serve.

Cook's tip... When you buy a pack of bagels, slice the fresh bagels in half and freeze them. The bagel halves can then simply be toasted from frozen so they're ready in an instant whenever you want them.

5 1/2
POINTS
VALUE

Spiced couscous salad

You may want to pack this salad in a lunch box and take it to work since it travels so well.

Serves 2 | **Takes 15** minutes | **10 *POINTS*** values per recipe | **366** calories per serving

*2 **eggs***
*100 g (3½ oz) dried **couscous***
25 g (1 oz) sultanas
½ teaspoon ground cumin
finely grated zest and juice of ½ a lemon
175 ml (6 fl oz) boiling water
*1 **carrot**, peeled and grated coarsely*
*6 **radishes**, trimmed, halved and sliced*
15 g (½ oz) sunflower seeds, toasted lightly

Method

1 Place the eggs in a small pan of cold water, bring to the boil and simmer for 7 minutes. Cool under cold running water, peel and cut into quarters.

2 Meanwhile, mix the couscous with the sultanas, cumin, lemon zest and juice and pour in the boiling water. Stir briefly to mix and then cover with a plate. Leave to stand and soften for 7 minutes.

3 Stir the carrot, radishes and sunflower seeds into the couscous and top with the hard-boiled eggs to serve.

Cook's tip... To toast the sunflower seeds, dry fry them in a non stick frying pan for 1–2 minutes, stirring the seeds until they are a pale golden colour and starting to smell toasted.

Smart ideas...

Preparing lunch to take to work, rather than buying it on the run, can save you money and ***POINTS*** values. Work colleagues are also bound to admire your delicious food.

5
POINTS
VALUE

Tricolore pasta salad

Prepare this colourful pasta salad the night before and pack it into a lunchbox, ready to take to work, or on a picnic.

Serves 1 | **Takes 12** minutes | **4½ *POINTS*** values per recipe | **291** calories per serving

40 g (1½ oz) dried mini **pasta** *shells*
60 g (2 oz) **broccoli**, *cut into tiny florets*
½ yellow or orange **pepper**, *de-seeded and diced*
100 g (3½ oz) **cherry tomatoes**, *halved*
25 g (1 oz) Edam cheese, cut into small dice
1 tablespoon shredded fresh **basil**
1 tablespoon low fat French dressing

Method

1 Bring a pan of water to the boil, add the pasta and cook for 6–7 minutes or until almost cooked. Add the broccoli to the pan and cook for 2 minutes longer.

2 Drain the pasta and broccoli and rinse in cold water. Drain again.

3 Mix the pepper, tomatoes, Edam, basil and French dressing together in a bowl. Stir in the pasta and broccoli and then serve.

Chicken, grape and potato salad

4 POINTS VALUE

This summery salad is a wonderful mixture of different flavours and textures. The grapes add a soft and sweet crunchiness and a light, creamy dressing brings it all together.

Serves 2 | **Takes 20** minutes | **8½ *POINTS*** values per recipe | **285** calories per serving

300 g (10½ oz) new **potatoes**, *diced*
125 g (4½ oz) **skinless boneless chicken breast**, *halved horizontally*
40 g (1½ oz) reduced fat mayonnaise
50 g (1¾ oz) **low fat natural yogurt**
1 tablespoon snipped fresh **chives**
½ teaspoon Dijon mustard (optional)
100 g (3½ oz) **red grapes**, *halved*
1 **Little Gem lettuce**, *leaves separated*
freshly ground black pepper

Method

1 Bring a lidded saucepan of water to the boil and cook the potatoes, covered, for 15 minutes or until tender. Drain.

2 Meanwhile, heat the grill to medium high and grill the chicken for 10–12 minutes until cooked through. Set aside to cool.

3 In a large bowl, mix the mayonnaise with the yogurt, chives and mustard, if using, adding pepper to taste. Stir in the new potatoes and grapes.

4 Slice the chicken and mix into the potato salad. Serve on a bed of Little Gem lettuce leaves.

Why not try... this delicious potato salad with 125 g (4½ oz) skinless and sliced leftover roast chicken, for 5 ***POINTS*** values per serving.

4
POINTS
VALUE

Rice noodle salad with prawns

Enjoy a wonderfully refreshing salad of soft noodles, crunchy vegetables and sweet prawns for lunch.

Serves 2 | **Takes 15** minutes | **13 *POINTS*** values per recipe | **427** calories per serving

125 g (4½ oz) dried thin **rice noodles**
3 heaped tablespoons chopped fresh **coriander**
50 g (1¾ oz) **mange tout***, sliced thinly*
1 large **carrot***, peeled and grated coarsely*
25 g (1 oz) peanuts, chopped finely
200 g (7 oz) cooked and peeled **prawns**

For the dressing
finely grated zest and juice of ½ a lime
1 tablespoon soy sauce
2 teaspoons light brown soft sugar
½ red **chilli***, de-seeded and diced*

Method

1 Bring a pan of water to the boil, remove from the heat and add the noodles. Soak for 5 minutes until tender. Drain and rinse in cold water. Drain again.
2 Mix the dressing ingredients together in a bowl and toss the noodles in the dressing. Add the coriander, mange tout, carrot and peanuts. Toss together well.
3 Divide between two bowls and serve topped with the prawns.

Smart ideas...

Try to buy fruit and vegetables in season – they'll taste better and be much cheaper too. You can often pick up bargains and then turn them into economical soups or fruit salads.

6½
POINTS
VALUE

chapter 3

midweek meals in minutes

When supper needs to be on the table in a hurry after a long day, you can rely on these **speedy recipes** to keep everyone **satisfied**. Choose from a delicious variety of quick meals such as Smoked Salmon Linguine, Beef Fajitas or Quick Herby Chicken Curry. They're all **ready in 30 minutes or less**.

Mango masala lamb steaks on page 48

Green velvet tagliatelle

Serve this quick pasta sauce with a zero *POINTS* value tomato salad.

Serves 4 | **Takes 15** minutes | **20½ *POINTS*** values per recipe | **307** calories per serving

250 g (9 oz) dried **tagliatelle**
275 g (9½ oz) frozen **peas**
2 **garlic cloves***, crushed*
150 ml (5 fl oz) hot vegetable stock
75 g (2¾ oz) **watercress***, chopped roughly*
75 g (2¾ oz) **low fat soft cheese**
25 g (1 oz) freshly grated Parmesan cheese
freshly ground black pepper

Method

1 Bring a pan of water to the boil. Cook the pasta for 7 minutes then add 100 g (3½ oz) of the peas. Cook for a further 2 minutes or until the pasta is tender.

2 Meanwhile, place the rest of the peas in a medium, lidded saucepan with the garlic and stock and cook, covered, for 5 minutes. Pile in the watercress, cover again and cook for 2 minutes until wilted. Stir in the soft cheese. Transfer to a liquidiser or use a hand held blender and blend to a smooth sauce.

3 Drain the pasta and peas and toss with the sauce and the grated cheese, plus plenty of black pepper. Serve immediately in warmed bowls.

Tomato, asparagus and basil fusilli

If you're looking for a supper that can be made from scratch in just a matter of minutes, try this speedy pasta dish.

Serves 2 | **Takes 15** minutes | **6 *POINTS*** values per recipe | **267** calories per serving

125 g (4½ oz) dried **pasta** *shells*
100 g (3½ oz) **asparagus** *tips, chopped*
low fat cooking spray
1 **garlic clove***, crushed*
250 g (9 oz) cherry **tomatoes***, halved*
½ teaspoon caster sugar
2 heaped tablespoons shredded fresh **basil**
freshly ground black pepper

Method

1 Bring a pan of water to the boil, add the pasta and cook for 12 minutes, adding the asparagus tips for the last 4 minutes.

2 Meanwhile, spray a lidded saucepan with cooking spray. Add the garlic and tomatoes and fry for 1 minute until starting to soften. Season with black pepper and stir in the sugar. Cover and cook for 4 minutes until the tomatoes form a sauce.

3 Drain the pasta and asparagus and toss together with the tomato sauce and the basil. Serve immediately.

3
POINTS
VALUE

Gratin of gnocchi with tomato and bacon

6 POINTS VALUE

8

As a quick meal, gnocchi make a nice change from pasta. They cook in just a couple of minutes and are very filling.

Serves 4 | **Takes 15** minutes | **23 *POINTS*** values per recipe | **325** calories per serving

low fat cooking spray
6 lean back bacon rashers, chopped
2 garlic cloves, crushed
1 bunch spring onions, sliced
4 fresh tomatoes, chopped roughly
500 g (1 lb 2 oz) fresh gnocchi
25 g (1 oz) freshly grated Parmesan cheese
freshly ground black pepper

Method

1 Preheat the grill. Heat a non stick frying pan on the hob and spray with the cooking spray. Fry the chopped bacon for 2–3 minutes then add the garlic and spring onions and stir fry for 1 minute more.
2 Add the tomatoes plus 4 tablespoons of water and cook for 4 minutes until the tomatoes have softened and broken down to make a sauce. Season with black pepper.
3 Meanwhile, bring a pan of water to the boil, add the gnocchi and cook for 2–3 minutes until they rise to the surface. Lift out using a draining spoon and transfer to a shallow baking dish.
4 Top with the tomato and bacon sauce and scatter with cheese. Grill for 2–3 minutes until the cheese is bubbling. Serve immediately.

Cook's tip... You don't always need to use a timer to cook the gnocchi – you'll know they are ready when they float to the surface of the pan.

Herb-crusted plaice with tomatoes

4 POINTS VALUE

7

Serve with 150 g (5½ oz) new potatoes per person and some mange tout on the side, for an additional 1½ ***POINTS*** values per serving.

Serves 2 | **Takes 15** minutes | **7½ *POINTS*** values per recipe | **291** calories per serving

low fat cooking spray
2 medium slices white bread
finely grated zest and juice of ½ a lemon
25 g (1 oz) low fat spread, melted
1 tablespoon chopped fresh parsley
1 tablespoon chopped fresh lemon thyme
2 x 150 g (5½ oz) plaice fillets
2 tomatoes, halved
freshly ground black pepper

Method

1 Preheat the grill to a medium heat and line the grill pan with foil. Spray with the cooking spray.
2 Roughly tear up the bread and then whizz to crumbs in a food processor. Mix with the lemon zest, half the lemon juice, the melted spread, herbs and black pepper.
3 Arrange the plaice fillets and the tomatoes side by side on the grill pan. Drizzle the rest of the lemon juice over the fish and then press the breadcrumb mixture firmly on to the plaice and the tomatoes.
4 Grill for 6–7 minutes until the topping is crisp and lightly browned, and the fish has cooked through. There is no need to turn the fish during cooking – it cooks through very easily. Serve immediately.

4
POINTS
VALUE

Quick herby chicken curry

The wonderful flavours of fresh herbs make this curry fragrant and delicious.

Serves 2 | **Takes 15** minutes | **6 *POINTS*** values per recipe | **219** calories per serving

low fat cooking spray
1 small **onion**, *sliced*
2 x 125 g (4½ oz) **skinless boneless chicken breast**, *diced*
2 **garlic cloves**, *crushed*
1 teaspoon grated root ginger
1 teaspoon garam masala or medium curry powder
2 teaspoons cornflour
150 g (5½ oz) **low fat natural yogurt**
1 tablespoon chopped fresh **mint**
3 heaped tablespoons chopped fresh **coriander**

Method

1 Heat a non stick frying pan until hot and spray with the cooking spray. Fry the onion for about 4 minutes, then push to one side and add the chicken to the pan. Cook for 3–4 minutes, stirring the chicken and onion around once or twice.

2 Add the garlic, ginger and garam masala or curry powder and cook for 1 minute, stirring. Reduce the heat to medium, and remove the pan from the hob.

3 Blend the cornflour with 1 teaspoon of cold water and then stir this into the yogurt. Gradually stir the yogurt mixture into the pan, one spoonful at a time. Return to the hob and gently bring to a simmer, taking care not to boil the sauce or it may curdle. Stir in the herbs just before serving.

Why not try... 250 g (9 oz) Quorn Deli Chicken Style Pieces instead of chicken, for 3 ***POINTS*** values per serving.

Smart ideas...

Try growing your own herbs, such as thyme, basil, parsley, chives and coriander, on a sunny windowsill – they'll always be handy and it's far more economical than buying packets of cut herbs from the supermarket that have a short shelf-life.

3 POINTS VALUE

Honeyed duck noodle bowl

This delicious Oriental style dish is a complete meal in a bowl.

Serves 2 | **Takes 20** minutes | **10½ *POINTS*** values per recipe | **390** calories per serving

low fat cooking spray
150 g (5½ oz) **skinless boneless duck breast**
2 rounded teaspoons clear honey
150 g (5½ oz) **baby corn***, sliced on the diagonal*
125 g (4½ oz) medium **egg noodles**
2.5 cm (1 inch) piece ginger, peeled and cut into matchsticks
1 tablespoon soy sauce
850 ml (1½ pints) hot chicken stock
50 g (1¾ oz) young leaf **spinach**
2 **spring onions***, sliced on the diagonal*

Method

1 Heat a non stick frying pan until hot and spray with the cooking spray. Pan fry the duck breast for 6 minutes on each side over a medium heat. Add the honey then immediately remove the pan from the hob and turn the duck over several times to coat in the honey. Set aside for 5 minutes.

2 Meanwhile, bring a pan of water to the boil, add the baby corn and noodles and cook for 4 minutes or until tender. While they are cooking, add the ginger and soy sauce to the chicken stock and set aside for the ginger to infuse.

3 Drain the noodles and corn and divide between two deep bowls. Top with the spinach and spring onions then pour the gingered stock all over.

4 Slice the duck breast thinly and arrange on top of the noodles and vegetables, drizzling with any juices from the pan.

Why not try... lean pork fillet instead of duck. Slice 150 g (5½ oz) pork fillet thinly and dust with 1 teaspoon of Chinese five spice powder. Fry for 3–4 minutes on each side in step 1 until cooked through but still juicy. The ***POINTS*** values will be the same.

Smart ideas...

Buy the best quality ingredients you can afford – you'll get the maximum amount of flavour and your food will be more satisfying and pleasurable.

5 1/2
POINTS
VALUE

Mango masala lamb steaks

A quick spice rub and a chutney topping give these lamb steaks a fantastic flavour.

Serves 4 | **Takes 30** minutes | **24½ *POINTS*** values per recipe | **385** calories per serving

900 g (2 lb) **potatoes**, *peeled and cut into 1 cm (½ inch) dice*
low fat cooking spray
1 **onion**, *sliced*
1 green **chilli**, *de-seeded and sliced*
2 teaspoons cumin seeds
2 teaspoons garam masala
4 x 125 g (4½ oz) **lean lamb leg steaks**, *trimmed of all fat*
80 g (3 oz) mango chutney

Method

1 Bring a saucepan of water to the boil, add the potatoes and parboil for 7 minutes. Drain then shake the potatoes to roughen the edges slightly.
2 While the potatoes are cooking, heat a large non stick frying pan, spray with the cooking spray and then cook the onion for 5 minutes, adding 1 tablespoon of water to help soften the onion.
3 Stir the potatoes, chilli and half of the cumin seeds in with the onion. Cook, stirring occasionally, for 15 minutes until tender and crisp.
4 Meanwhile, preheat the grill to medium high. Mix the rest of the cumin seeds with the garam masala. Spray the lamb with the cooking spray and coat in the spice mixture. Grill for 6 minutes then turn and grill for another 2 minutes. Top each lamb steak with chutney and then cook for a final 4 minutes.
5 Serve the lamb on the crisp, spiced potatoes.

Cook's tip... Shaking parboiled potatoes in the pan roughens up the edges and creates more surface area for crisping up when pan-fried.

Smoked salmon linguine

Serve with a mixed leaf and rocket salad, dressed with a little lemon juice, for no additional ***POINTS*** values.

Serves 2 | **Takes 15** minutes | **10½ *POINTS*** values per recipe | **358** calories per serving

125 g (4½ oz) dried **linguine**
1 **egg**
60 g (2 oz) **low fat soft cheese**
finely grated zest and juice of ½ a small lemon
2 tablespoons snipped fresh **chives**
60 g (2 oz) **smoked salmon**, *sliced into strips*
freshly ground black pepper

Method

1 Bring a pan of water to the boil and cook the pasta for 12 minutes or according to the packet instructions until tender.
2 Meanwhile, in a small bowl, beat the egg with the soft cheese then stir in the lemon zest, juice, chives and smoked salmon.
3 Drain the pasta and return to the saucepan. Mix in the smoked salmon mixture, tossing well to mix thoroughly. Season with the black pepper and serve in warmed bowls.

Cook's tip... Economical smoked salmon trimmings are perfect for this recipe, and cost a lot less than the more expensive sliced smoked salmon.

5
POINTS
VALUE

Minted lamb pittas with tzatziki

Lamb with mint makes a classic Sunday roast, but here's a quick and easy recipe for a midweek meal. Serve with a zero *POINTS* value tomato and red onion salad.

Serves 2 | **Takes 15** minutes | ***10 POINTS*** values per recipe | **293** calories per serving

200 g (7 oz) **lean lamb leg steaks**, *trimmed of all fat*
½ teaspoon dried **mint**
2 wholemeal pitta breads
1 **Little Gem lettuce**, *leaves separated*
1 **carrot**, *peeled and grated coarsely*
freshly ground black pepper

For the tzatziki
a pinch of dried **mint**
100 g (3½ oz) **0% fat Greek yogurt**
50 g (1¾ oz) **cucumber**, *diced*

Method

1 Preheat the grill to medium high, and line the grill pan with foil. Season the lamb with black pepper and rub in the dried mint. Grill for 5 minutes on each side or until cooked to your liking. Leave to rest for a few minutes before slicing thinly.

2 Meanwhile, to make the tzatziki, mix the dried mint with the yogurt and cucumber. Lightly toast the pittas under the grill then cut each one in half to form two pockets.

3 Spoon in some tzatziki, tuck in a few lettuce leaves and grated carrot and finally, stuff in the lamb to serve.

Spiced salmon with pea purée

Fish is so quick to cook that it makes the perfect speedy supper. Adding spices livens up the meal for no extra effort.

Serves 4 | **Takes 15** minutes | ***23½ POINTS*** values per recipe | **339** calories per serving

1 tablespoon medium curry powder
1 teaspoon cumin seeds
juice of ½ a lemon
4 x 125 g (4½ oz) skinless **salmon** *fillets*
low fat cooking spray
400 g (14 oz) frozen **peas**
2 heaped tablespoons chopped fresh **coriander**
2 tablespoons half fat crème fraîche
2 tablespoons **skimmed milk**
freshly ground black pepper

Method

1 In a small bowl, mix the curry powder, cumin seeds and lemon juice to a paste and spread over both sides of the salmon. Season with the black pepper.

2 Heat a non stick frying pan until hot and spray with the cooking spray. Add the salmon fillets and cook for 4 minutes on each side over a medium heat until lightly caramelised and just cooked through.

3 Meanwhile in a saucepan, cook the frozen peas in boiling water for 2–3 minutes until tender. Drain and transfer to a food processor with the coriander, crème fraîche and milk. Whizz to a rough purée. Season with black pepper and serve with the spiced salmon.

6
POINTS
VALUE

Pan-fried turkey and ham escalopes

Spreading a layer of garlic and herb soft cheese between the turkey and ham adds a luxurious dimension to this recipe. Serve with steamed broccoli, for no extra *POINTS* values.

Serves 2 | **Takes 20** minutes | **7½ *POINTS*** values per recipe | **242** calories per serving

2 x 125 g (4½ oz) **turkey breast steaks**
40 g (1½ oz) **low fat soft cheese with garlic and herbs**
4 slices **wafer thin smoked ham**
1 teaspoon olive oil
1 tablespoon plain flour, seasoned
150 ml (5 fl oz) hot chicken stock
2 teaspoons lemon juice

Method

1 Place the turkey steaks between two layers of clingfilm and flatten, using a rolling pin or frying pan, to 5 mm (¼ inch) thick. Cut each steak in half, spread each piece with the soft cheese then use a cocktail stick to secure a slice of ham to each piece of turkey.

2 Add the oil to a non stick frying pan and heat the pan until hot. Dip the escalopes in the seasoned flour and fry for 3 minutes on each side, cooking the ham side first.

3 Tip any remaining seasoned flour into the pan and stir into the pan juices. Blend in the stock and lemon juice and bubble rapidly for 2 minutes.

4 Serve immediately, removing the cocktail sticks before eating.

Cook's tip... A rolling pin is the easiest implement to use to flatten the turkey breast steaks. However, you could also use the base of a small heavy pan, or the rounded sides of a can of baked beans (or similar).

Smart ideas...

Invest in a proper non stick frying pan and saucepan – they don't need to be expensive and they make it so much easier to cook healthy food properly.

4
POINTS
VALUE

Tangy chicken with crushed potatoes

4 POINTS VALUE

Tender sugar snap peas are a good zero ***POINTS*** value vegetable to serve with this recipe.

Serves 4 | **Takes 25 minutes** | **16 *POINTS*** values per recipe | **271** calories per serving

600 g (1 lb 5 oz) baby **new potatoes**
4 x 125 g (4½ oz) **skinless boneless chicken breast**, *slashed*
1 tablespoon Dijon mustard
1 tablespoon Worcestershire sauce
low fat cooking spray
finely grated zest and juice of ½ a lemon
2 tablespoons chopped fresh **parsley**
2 teaspoons extra virgin olive oil
freshly ground black pepper

Method

1 Bring a pan of water to the boil, add the potatoes and cook for 15–20 minutes until tender. Preheat the grill to medium and line the grill pan with foil.
2 Meanwhile, season the chicken breasts with black pepper. Mix the mustard and Worcestershire sauce together and brush on to both sides of the chicken. Spray with the cooking spray and grill for 15 minutes, turning once, or until cooked through.
3 When the potatoes are ready, drain then return to the pan. Use a wooden spoon to lightly crush the potatoes then mix in the lemon zest and juice, parsley, olive oil and black pepper. Serve with the grilled chicken.

Cook's tip... Slashing the chicken breasts with a sharp knife means that the flavours of the basting sauce can infuse the chicken, without the need for marinating.

Beef fajitas

Serve with a zero ***POINTS*** value salad made of crunchy cucumber, tomato and crisp lettuce.

Serves 2 | **Takes 15** minutes | **13 *POINTS*** values per recipe | **452** calories per serving

low fat cooking spray
200 g (7 oz) **lean beef escalopes**, *sliced into strips*
1 **onion**, *sliced*
½ red **pepper**, *de-seeded and sliced*
½ green **pepper**, *de-seeded and sliced*
100 g (3½ oz) **mushrooms**, *sliced*
½ teaspoon Spicy Season-All
4 medium soft flour tortillas
4 tablespoons **0% fat Greek yogurt**

Method

1 Heat a non stick frying pan until hot and spray with the cooking spray. Stir fry the strips of beef for 3 minutes, and then remove to a plate.
2 Add the onion and peppers to the frying pan and stir fry over a high heat for 3 minutes. Mix in the mushrooms and add 2 tablespoons of water. Reduce the heat to medium and cook for 2 minutes.
3 Return the beef to the pan and sprinkle in the spicy seasoning. Cook for 1 minute, stirring to mix.
4 Warm through the tortillas following the packet instructions. Serve two tortillas per person, to roll around the fajita mixture, topped with a tablespoon of yogurt.

Why not try... replacing the beef with 1 courgette, sliced into strips, and increase the mushrooms to 200 g (7 oz), for 4½ ***POINTS*** values per serving.

Cook's tip... Spicy Season-All is a spice blend that is very easy to find in supermarkets. It's a mixture of ground cumin, coriander, chilli powder, oregano, dried garlic, dried onion and paprika.

6 1/2
POINTS
VALUE

Rosemary pork fillet with lemon rice

(12)

This is a very easy way to cook risotto rice.

Serves 4 | **Takes 30** minutes | **29 *POINTS*** values per recipe | **448** calories per serving

500 g (1 lb 2 oz) **pork fillet**, *trimmed of all fat*
finely grated zest and juice of a lemon
1½ tablespoons finely chopped fresh **rosemary**
low fat cooking spray
2 **leeks**, *sliced*
250 g (9 oz) risotto rice
700 ml (1¼ pints) hot chicken stock
25 g (1 oz) freshly grated Parmesan cheese
freshly ground black pepper

Method

1 Preheat the oven to Gas Mark 6/200°C/fan oven 180°C. Drizzle half the lemon juice over the pork and then rub 1 tablespoon of the rosemary and half the lemon zest into the meat. Season with black pepper. Place the pork in a roasting tin sprayed with the cooking spray and roast in the oven for 25 minutes or until the juices run clear when the thickest part of the fillet is pierced.

2 Meanwhile, spray a large saucepan with the cooking spray. Add the leeks and cook for 2 minutes then add the rest of the rosemary and the risotto rice, stirring for 1 minute.

3 Pour in the hot stock and bring to the boil. Simmer, uncovered, for 18 minutes or until the rice is tender. Stir in the cheese, plus the rest of the lemon zest and juice. Season to taste.

4 Carve the pork into thin slices and serve on a bed of the lemon and leek rice.

Cook's tip... If you've got time, before carving the pork into slices, let the pork fillet rest for 5–10 minutes once it has come out of the oven, covered loosely with foil. This will allow the cooking juices that have bubbled up during roasting to be re-absorbed into the meat, so that it will be more tender and moist.

Why not try... slices of courgette, griddled using low fat cooking spray as a lovely accompaniment to the pork and rice, for no additional ***POINTS*** values.

7 1/2
POINTS
VALUE

chapter

4

Cooking for one

These tasty recipes are so easy, you'll be inspired again and again to cook **something lovely for yourself**. After work, relax and unwind with a delicious bowl of Teriyaki Beef Udon or Moroccan Lamb and Green Bean Stir Fry – they're both ready in 15 minutes or less. Or bake some fresh fish and enjoy the **comforting flavours** of the Chinese Cod and Mushroom Parcel.

Cinnamon, mint and lemon pork on page 68

Chicken chilli fried rice

This is ideal with 150 g (5½ oz) leftover cold rice as it's less likely to stick to the pan than freshly cooked rice.

Serves 1 | **Takes 30** minutes | **5 *POINTS*** values per recipe | **402** calories

- *60 g (2 oz)* **brown rice**
- *low fat cooking spray*
- *125 g (4½ oz)* **skinless boneless chicken breast**, *diced*
- *1 red* **pepper**, *de-seeded and diced*
- *½ red or green* **chilli**, *de-seeded and diced*
- *1* **garlic clove**, *crushed*
- *3* **spring onions**, *sliced*
- *juice of ½ a lime*
- *2 heaped tablespoons chopped fresh* **coriander**

Method

1 Bring a pan of water to the boil, add the rice and cook according to the packet instructions until tender. Drain and rinse well in cold water.

2 Heat a non stick frying pan until hot and spray with the cooking spray. Add the chicken and stir fry for 2 minutes over a high heat. Mix in the pepper and continue to cook for another 3 minutes.

3 Scatter in the chilli, garlic and spring onions. Stir fry for 1 minute then stir in the rice and the lime juice. Stir fry for 2 minutes until the rice is thoroughly heated through. Mix in the coriander just before serving.

Why not try... a vegetarian version, replacing the chicken with 75 g (2¾ oz) marinated tofu pieces for 6 ***POINTS*** values.

Cook's tip... If you like it hot, keep the seeds in the chilli.

Indian omelette

This is a great way to jazz up an omelette and it's delicious with a zero ***POINTS*** value salad.

Serves 1 | **Takes 10** minutes | **2½ *POINTS*** values per recipe | **225** calories

- *low fat cooking spray*
- *½ small* **onion**, *sliced thinly*
- *½ red or green* **chilli**, *de-seeded and diced*
- *2* **eggs**
- *a pinch of ground cumin*
- *1* **tomato**, *diced*
- *2 heaped tablespoons chopped fresh* **coriander**
- *salt and freshly ground black pepper*

Method

1 Heat a non stick frying pan until hot and spray with the cooking spray. Fry the onion and chilli for 4–5 minutes, adding a splash of water as needed to prevent the onion from sticking and burning.

2 Beat the eggs with 1 tablespoon of water, the ground cumin and seasoning. Stir in the tomato and coriander then pour this mixture into the frying pan.

3 Cook over a medium heat until the omelette is golden underneath and just set on top. Turn out on to a warmed plate.

Why not try... something a little different by serving the omelette rolled up inside a medium chapati or soft flour tortilla, for 2½ extra ***POINTS*** values.

2 $\frac{1}{2}$ POINTS VALUE

Chinese five spiced trout

3 POINTS VALUE

A serving of 60 g (2 oz) dried egg noodles, cooked according to the packet instructions, makes an ideal accompaniment to the Oriental flavours of this meal, for 3 additional ***POINTS*** values.

Serves 1 | **Takes 15** minutes | **2 *POINTS*** values per recipe | **309** calories

low fat cooking spray
150 g (5½ oz) skinned **trout fillet**
1 teaspoon Chinese five spice
75 g (2¾ oz) **mange tout***, halved on the diagonal*
75 g (2¾ oz) **baby corn***, each cut into 3 or 4 pieces*
½ teaspoon finely grated root ginger
3 tablespoons oyster sauce

Method

1 Heat a non stick frying pan until hot and spray with the cooking spray. Dust the trout with the Chinese five spice on both sides. Fry for 3 minutes on each side over a medium heat. Transfer to a warmed plate and cover with foil to keep warm.

2 Increase the heat under the frying pan and spray again with the cooking spray. Stir fry the mange tout, baby corn and ginger with 1 tablespoon of water for 2 minutes.

3 Add the oyster sauce plus 3 tablespoons of water to the pan. Cook for 2 minutes more, until the vegetables are tender and the sauce has thickened to a coating consistency. Serve with the trout.

Smoked haddock with chive sauce

A real comfort food supper, prepared in a matter of minutes. Serve with steamed broccoli, for no additional ***POINTS*** values.

Serves 1 | **Takes 12** minutes | **4½ *POINTS*** values per recipe | **282** calories

175 g (6 oz) skinned **smoked haddock**
125 ml (4 fl oz) **skimmed milk**
2 teaspoons cornflour
30 g (1¼ oz) half fat crème fraîche
1 tablespoon snipped fresh **chives**
a squeeze of lemon juice
freshly ground black pepper

Method

1 Place the smoked haddock in a medium lidded pan, pour in the milk and season with black pepper. Cover and bring to a simmer then poach gently for about 5 minutes, depending on the thickness of the haddock, until the fish flakes easily. Lift out on to a hot plate and keep warm, reserving the milk.

2 Blend the cornflour with a little cold water and then stir into the hot milk in the pan. Bring to a simmer, stirring constantly until thickened. Simmer for 1 minute. Stir in the crème fraîche, chives and lemon juice, to taste. Pour over the smoked haddock to serve.

4 1/2
POINTS
VALUE

One pot rosemary chicken pasta

This speedy casserole is a complete meal with hardly any washing up.

Serves 1 | **Takes 10** minutes to prepare, **15** minutes to cook | **4 *POINTS*** values per recipe | **363** calories

- *low fat cooking spray*
- *125 g (4½ oz)* **skinless boneless chicken breast**, *diced*
- *½* **onion**, *chopped*
- *1 small* **courgette**, *diced*
- *1* **garlic clove**, *crushed*
- *210 g can chopped* **tomatoes**
- *½ tablespoon chopped fresh* **rosemary** *or ½ teaspoon dried rosemary*
- *40 g (1½ oz) dried* **penne**
- *150 ml (5 fl oz) boiling water*
- *salt and freshly ground black pepper*

Method

1 Heat a lidded, non stick saucepan until hot and spray with the cooking spray. Brown the chicken and onion for 2 minutes. Add the diced courgette and garlic and cook for 2 minutes more.

2 Add the tomatoes, rosemary, pasta and boiling water to the pan and season to taste. Bring to the boil and cook, partially covered, for 15 minutes or until the pasta is tender.

Cook's tip... You can use half a 400 g can of chopped tomatoes and freeze the leftover tomatoes for another meal.

Why not try... replacing the chicken with 125 g (4½ oz) Quorn Chicken Style Pieces for a vegetarian version of this recipe, for 4 ***POINTS*** values.

Cider and mustard chicken

This is delicious with a medium (60 g/2 oz) portion of dried brown rice, cooked according to the packet instructions. Add 50 g (1¾ oz) chopped green beans, for the final 3 minutes of cooking time, for an additional 3 ***POINTS*** values.

Serves 1 | **Takes 20** minutes | **3½ *POINTS*** values per recipe | **285** calories

- *low fat cooking spray*
- *125 g (4½ oz)* **skinless boneless chicken breast**
- *1 small* **onion**, *sliced*
- *1* **garlic clove**, *crushed*
- *150 ml (5 fl oz) medium cider*
- *1 teaspoon cornflour*
- *1 teaspoon coarse grain mustard*
- *15 g (½ oz)* **low fat soft cheese**

Method

1 Heat a small, lidded, non stick frying pan until hot and spray with the cooking spray. Place the chicken in the pan and scatter the onion around the chicken. Fry the chicken for 2 minutes on each side, stirring the onions occasionally. Add the garlic and cook for 1 minute more.

2 Pour the cider into the pan and bubble rapidly for 2 minutes until slightly reduced. Blend the cornflour with a little cold water then add to the cider, followed by the mustard, stirring until thickened.

3 Cover the pan and simmer for 8 minutes, until the chicken is cooked. Stir the soft cheese into the sauce just before serving to give a creamy finish.

Why not try... a vegetarian version of this recipe, using two Quorn Chicken Style Fillets, cooked from frozen, instead of the chicken breast, for 3 ***POINTS*** values.

3 1/2
POINTS
VALUE

Chinese cod and mushroom parcel

Serve with a medium portion (60 g/2 oz) dried Thai jasmine rice (cooked according to the packet instructions), to soak up the fragrant juices, for an additional 3 *POINTS* values.

Serves 1 | **Takes 5** minutes to prepare, **15** minutes to cook | **3 *POINTS*** values per recipe | **203** calories

low fat cooking spray
175 g (6 oz) skinless **cod loin**
1 rounded teaspoon clear honey
1 tablespoon soy sauce
1 small **garlic clove***, sliced*
¼ red **chilli***, de-seeded and sliced*
3 slices root ginger, peeled and cut into matchsticks
1 head **pak choi***, halved*
60 g (2 oz) **chestnut mushrooms***, sliced thickly*

Method

1 Preheat the oven to Gas Mark 6/200°C/fan oven 180°C.
2 Tear off a large rectangle of foil from a roll and lightly spray the dull side with the cooking spray. Place the cod in the centre of the foil.
3 Mix the honey, soy sauce, garlic, chilli and ginger together and spoon half over the cod. Sit the pak choi and mushrooms on top of the fish and drizzle with the remaining soy mixture.
4 Fold the foil up around the fish and vegetables, crimping and folding the edges tightly to seal. Place on a baking tray and cook for 15 minutes, until the fish flakes easily.

Why not try... a 125 g (4½ oz) skinless boneless chicken breast fillet instead of the cod, for 2½ ***POINTS*** values per serving. The chicken will need to be cooked for an extra 5 minutes.

Ⓥ **...a vegetarian version**, replacing the cod with two frozen Quorn fillets. Lightly brown the Quorn fillets in cooking spray for 2 minutes on each side before placing them on the foil, then cook the sealed parcel for 20 minutes. This will be 2 ***POINTS*** values.

Smart ideas...

If you're shopping for yourself, ask the fishmonger or butcher to prepare single portions.

3
POINTS
VALUE

Cinnamon, mint and lemon pork

Fine green beans are a good accompaniment to the pork and couscous, for no additional *POINTS* values.

Serves 1 | **Takes 15** minutes + **20** minutes marinating (optional) | **6 *POINTS*** values per recipe | **416** calories

finely grated zest and juice of ½ a lemon
1 tablespoon finely chopped fresh **mint**
¼ teaspoon ground cinnamon
125 g (4½ oz) **lean pork steak**, *trimmed of all fat*
low fat cooking spray
50 g (1¾ oz) dried **couscous**
25 g (1 oz) ready to eat semi dried apricots, chopped
100 ml (3½ fl oz) boiling water

Method

1 Mix half of the lemon zest, juice and mint with the cinnamon and then rub this mixture on to the pork. The pork steak can either be cooked immediately, or for a fuller flavour, set aside, covered, for up to 20 minutes.

2 Heat a non stick frying pan until hot and spray with the cooking spray. Fry the pork steak for 4 minutes on each side over a low to medium heat, until cooked through.

3 Meanwhile, place the couscous in a bowl with the apricots and the rest of the lemon zest, juice and mint. Pour in the boiling water and stir. Cover the bowl with a plate or use clingfilm and leave to stand for 6–7 minutes until softened.

4 Serve the pork on a bed of couscous.

Teriyaki beef udon

This Japanese dish uses thick udon noodles, a classic Japanese ingredient.

Serves 1 | **Takes 15** minutes | **6 *POINTS*** values per recipe | **453** calories

low fat cooking spray
125 g (4½ oz) **lean rump steak**, *trimmed of all fat*
½ red **onion**, *sliced*
50 g (1¾ oz) **sugar snap peas**, *halved lengthways*
75 g (2¾ oz) **mushrooms**, *sliced*
2 tablespoons teriyaki marinade
1 teaspoon cornflour
150 g pack pre-cooked **udon noodles**

Method

1 Heat a non stick frying pan until hot and spray with the cooking spray. Fry the steak for 2½–3 minutes on each side over a high heat, then transfer to a warm plate and leave to rest.

2 Add the onion to the pan and fry for 1 minute then add the sugar snaps and mushrooms plus 1 tablespoon of water. Stir fry for 2 minutes. Mix the teriyaki marinade with the cornflour and 4 tablespoons of cold water, then add to the frying pan and cook for 1 minute.

3 Mix the udon noodles into the sauce and vegetables. Cook for 1–2 minutes until heated through. Slice the steak thinly and serve on top of the noodles.

Why not try... leaving out the steak and increasing the mushrooms to 150 g (5½ oz). Add 75 g (2¾ oz) baby corn in step 2 with the mushrooms, for 3½ ***POINTS*** values.

6
POINTS
VALUE

Mushroom and chick pea gratin

4½ POINTS VALUE

This richly flavoured mixture of mushrooms and pulses with a delicious crisp gratin topping is good served with steamed broccoli, for no additional *POINTS* values.

Serves 1 | **Takes 15** minutes | **4½ *POINTS*** values per recipe | **344** calories

low fat cooking spray
200 g (7 oz) open cup **mushrooms**, *halved*
150 ml (5 fl oz) hot vegetable stock
½ teaspoon ground cumin
1 tablespoon tomato purée
½ x 410 g can **chick peas**, *drained and rinsed*
a squeeze of lemon juice
25 g (1 oz) fresh breadcrumbs
25 g (1 oz) low fat mature cheese, grated finely
freshly ground black pepper

Method

1 Heat a lidded saucepan until hot, spray with the cooking spray and add the mushrooms plus 1 tablespoon of the stock. Cook, covered, for 3 minutes then remove the lid and cook for 1 minute more to evaporate the juices. Preheat the grill to medium.

2 Stir the cumin and tomato purée into the mushrooms and cook for 1 minute. Add the chick peas and the rest of the stock and simmer, uncovered, for 4 minutes. Season with black pepper and add lemon juice to taste. Tip the mushroom and chick pea mixture into an ovenproof gratin dish.

3 Mix the breadcrumbs and cheese together and scatter evenly over the dish. Grill for 2–3 minutes until golden brown.

Moroccan lamb and green bean stir fry

Serve this fragrant stir fry with 60 g (2 oz) dried brown rice or 60 g (2 oz) dried couscous, cooked according to the packet instructions, for an additional 3 *POINTS* values.

Serves 1 | **Takes 10** minutes | **3 *POINTS*** values per recipe | **184** calories

low fat cooking spray
125 g (4½ oz) **lean lamb leg steak**, *trimmed of all fat and sliced thinly*
¼ teaspoon ground cumin
a pinch of ground cinnamon
75 g (2¾ oz) **green beans**, *halved*
1 ripe **tomato**, *chopped roughly*
freshly ground black pepper

Method

1 Heat a lidded, non stick frying pan until hot and spray with the cooking spray. Season the lamb with black pepper and stir fry over a high heat for 3 minutes until browned.

2 Add the cumin and cinnamon, followed by the green beans and tomato plus 2 tablespoons of water. Cover the pan and cook over a medium heat for 4–5 minutes, stirring once or twice, until the beans are tender but still have a bit of crunch left. Serve immediately.

Why not try... using 125 g (4½ oz) skinless chicken breast fillet instead of lamb, for 2 ***POINTS*** values.

3
POINTS
VALUE

Tandoori lamb kebabs with minted rice

The tandoori spice flavours the lamb without the need for marinating, but if you do have time to marinate for half an hour or so, the lamb will become even more flavoursome and tender.

Serves 1 | **Takes 25** minutes | **6½ *POINTS*** values per recipe | **442** calories

60 g (2 oz) **brown basmati rice**
¼ teaspoon dried **mint**
150 ml (5 fl oz) boiling water
75 g (2¾ oz) **low fat natural yogurt**
1½ teaspoons tandoori spice blend
1 teaspoon lemon juice
125 g (4½ oz) **lean lamb leg steak**, *trimmed of all fat and cut into bite sized pieces*
½ red or green **pepper**, *de-seeded and cut into bite sized pieces*
75 g (2¾ oz) button **mushrooms**
low fat cooking spray

Method

1 Place the rice and half of the mint in a lidded saucepan with the boiling water. Bring to the boil, stir once then cover and cook, undisturbed, for 25 minutes over a very low heat until all the water has been absorbed and the rice is tender.

2 Meanwhile, mix 50 g (1¾ oz) of the yogurt with the tandoori spice blend, lemon juice and remaining mint. Stir the lamb and peppers into the spiced yogurt, along with the mushrooms. Preheat the grill to medium.

3 Thread the lamb and vegetables on to two metal skewers. Spray with the cooking spray and grill for 12 minutes, turning halfway through.

4 Stir the remaining yogurt into the hot rice and serve with the kebabs.

Why not try... making tandoori vegetable kebabs by leaving out the lamb and increasing the mushrooms to 150 g (5½ oz) and adding a small courgette, cut into chunky slices, for 3½ ***POINTS*** values.

Smart ideas...

While cooking, why not prepare a meal for another night at the same time? Cover meat in a marinade and pop it straight into the freezer in a freezer bag. The meat will then marinate while defrosting.

6 1/2
POINTS
VALUE

chapter 5

Vegetarian

With a fantastic selection of **intensely flavoured** meat-free meals, this chapter has **something satisfying for everyone**, ranging from classics with a twist such as Sausage and Apple Toad in the Hole with Onion Gravy to the more modern Portobello Mushroom Burgers. And to spice up dinner time, try the delicious Potato, Spinach and Cauliflower Curry or Vegetable Pad Thai.

Portobello mushroom burger on page 80

Zesty veggie fried rice

10

The delicious combination of lemon, ginger and chilli gives this colourful stir fry a fresh and zingy flavour. Cashew nuts add a welcome crunch.

Serves 2 | **Takes 40** minutes | **10½ *POINTS*** values per recipe | **361** calories per serving

125 g (4½ oz) **brown basmati rice**
low fat cooking spray
25 g (1 oz) cashews, chopped
1 **courgette***, diced*
150 g (5½ oz) **mushrooms***, sliced*
6 **spring onions***, sliced*
1 teaspoon grated root ginger
1 **garlic clove***, crushed*
1 red **chilli***, de-seeded and chopped*
100 g (3½ oz) frozen **peas**
finely grated zest and juice of ½ a lemon

Method

1 Bring a pan of water to the boil, add the rice and cook for 25 minutes or until tender.

2 After about 20 minutes, heat a wok or large frying pan until hot and spray with the cooking spray. Stir fry the cashews until golden brown then tip into a small bowl.

3 Add the courgettes and mushrooms to the wok or frying pan and stir fry for 3–4 minutes before adding the spring onions, ginger, garlic and chilli, and cook for 1 minute, stirring. Mix in the frozen peas and cook for 1 minute more.

4 Drain the rice and rinse in cold water. Drain again. Add to the wok or frying pan with the lemon zest and juice. Stir fry for 2 minutes or until piping hot, then serve in warmed bowls, topped with the cashews.

Cook's tip... Brown rice takes a little longer to cook than white rice. However, you can make life much easier by cooking several portions of rice at once. Spread out the drained, cooked rice in a large shallow dish to cool and then freeze individual portions weighing 150 g (5½ oz) for 3 ***POINTS*** values each. 6

Why not try... ringing the changes by swapping the vegetables in the recipe for other zero ***POINTS*** value vegetables such as peppers, baby corn and mange tout.

5
POINTS
VALUE

Easy mushroom risotto

5 POINTS VALUE

If the thought of standing over a pan of risotto, constantly stirring and adding hot stock doesn't appeal, don't despair. With this simplified version, you only need to stir a couple of times and the risotto will be lovely, creamy and soft.

Serves 4 | **Takes 15** minutes to prepare, **20** minutes to cook | **19 *POINTS*** values per recipe | **317** calories per serving

25 g (1 oz) low fat spread
1 onion, chopped finely
350 g (12 oz) mushrooms, chopped
250 g (9 oz) dried Arborio risotto rice
850 ml (1½ pints) hot vegetable stock
25 g (1 oz) freshly grated Parmesan cheese
60 g (2 oz) low fat soft cheese
1 tablespoon snipped fresh chives
freshly ground black pepper

Method

1 Melt the low fat spread in a large, lidded, non stick saucepan. Stir in the onion plus 2 tablespoons of water. Cover and cook for 5 minutes until softened. Add the mushrooms, season with black pepper and cook, covered, for 3 minutes or until tender.

2 Stir in the rice with the mushrooms and cook, stirring, for 1 minute. Pour in the hot stock and simmer, uncovered, for 18–20 minutes, stirring occasionally, until the rice is tender.

3 Mix in the Parmesan cheese and soft cheese then serve in warmed bowls, with the chives scattered on top.

Pesto and green vegetable gnocchi

4½ POINTS VALUE

Serve with a zero *POINTS* value tomato and red onion salad to complete your meal.

Serves 2 | **Takes 10** minutes | **9½ *POINTS*** values per recipe | **330** calories per serving

100 g (3½ oz) fine green beans, cut in half
100 g (3½ oz) small broccoli florets
250 g (9 oz) fresh gnocchi
2 tablespoons green pesto
30 g (1¼ oz) low fat soft cheese
50 g (1¾ oz) young leaf spinach

Method

1 Bring two pans of water to the boil. Add the beans to one pan and cook for 3 minutes then add the broccoli to the same pan and cook for a further 3 minutes.

2 Once the broccoli has been added to the first pan, add the gnocchi to the second pan and cook for 2 minutes until the gnocchi float to the surface.

3 Drain the vegetables and the gnocchi, reserving 2 tablespoons of the vegetable cooking liquid. Stir the pesto and soft cheese together in one of the pans, adding the reserved cooking liquid to make a sauce of coating consistency. Gently toss together with the vegetables and gnocchi, mixing in the spinach. Serve in warm bowls.

Cook's tip... Jars of pesto often get forgotten in the back of the fridge and have to be thrown out. Instead, buy fresh pesto and freeze it as individual portions in an ice cube tray. 1 tablespoon (15 g/½ oz) of fresh pesto is 1½ ***POINTS*** values. Once frozen, turn the cubes of pesto out into a freezer bag, ready to use when needed.

4 1/2
POINTS
VALUE

07719 663422

Portobello mushroom burgers

3½ POINTS VALUE

7

The combination of herby baked mushrooms and houmous is truly sublime as a light meal.

Serves 4 | **Takes 10** minutes to prepare, **20** minutes to cook | **14 *POINTS*** values per recipe | **299** calories per serving

1 heaped tablespoon chopped fresh **thyme**
1 **garlic clove***, crushed*
finely grated zest and juice of ½ a lemon
4 extra large portobello or flat **mushrooms**
low fat cooking spray
4 x 75 g (2¾ oz) ciabatta rolls
75 g (2¾ oz) reduced fat houmous
50 g (1¾ oz) **0% fat Greek yogurt**
2 beef **tomatoes***, sliced*
40 g (1½ oz) **baby leaf salad**
freshly ground black pepper

Method

1 Preheat the oven to Gas Mark 6/200°C/fan oven 180°C. In a small bowl, mix the thyme, garlic, lemon zest and juice with black pepper and 1 tablespoon of water. Spray both sides of the mushrooms with the cooking spray and place in a roasting tin, stalk side up. Drizzle on the herb and lemon mixture, then cover the roasting tin with foil.

2 Put the roasting tin with the mushrooms in the oven, along with the rolls placed on top of the foil to warm through, for 10 minutes. Remove the rolls. Take the foil off the mushrooms and cook for a further 10 minutes.

3 Meanwhile, mix together the houmous and yogurt with a seasoning of black pepper.

4 Split the rolls open and spread with the houmous mixture. Add a few slices of tomato and a cooked mushroom to each one, plus a small handful of salad leaves. Serve immediately.

Beany moussaka

Serve with a salad of diced cucumber and chopped tomatoes dressed with a little lemon juice, for no extra ***POINTS*** values.

Serves 4 | **Takes 25** minutes to prepare, **30** minutes to cook | **11½ *POINTS*** values per recipe | **231** calories per serving

1 **aubergine***, cut into 1 cm (½ inch) slices*
low fat cooking spray
1 **onion***, chopped*
2 **garlic cloves***, crushed*
½ teaspoon ground cinnamon
400 g can chopped **tomatoes**
410 g can green **lentils***, rinsed and drained*
410 g can **black eye beans***, rinsed and drained*
1 **egg***, beaten*
300 g (10½ oz) **0% fat Greek yogurt**
2 **tomatoes***, sliced*
freshly ground black pepper

Method

1 Preheat the grill to a medium heat. Spray the aubergine with the cooking spray and grill for 3–4 minutes on each side until golden brown and tender. Set aside. Preheat the oven to Gas Mark 6/200°C/fan oven 180°C.

2 Meanwhile, heat a lidded, non stick saucepan until hot and spray with the cooking spray. Cook the onion for 2 minutes then add 2 tablespoons of water and cook, covered, for 3 minutes.

3 Stir in the garlic, cinnamon and tomatoes. Simmer for 3 minutes, uncovered. Add the lentils and beans and cook for a further 2 minutes. Tip into a 20 cm (8 inch) square baking dish and top with the grilled aubergine.

4 Mix the egg and yogurt together, season and pour over the aubergine. Arrange the tomato slices on top and bake in the oven for 30 minutes.

3
POINTS
VALUE

Welsh leek and cheese pasta bake

6½ POINTS VALUE

Serve this pasta bake with the Broccoli with Cheese and Tomatoes side dish (on page 158), for an additional ½ ***POINTS*** value per serving.

Serves 4 | **Takes 20** minutes to prepare, **20** minutes to cook | **26½ *POINTS*** values per recipe | **433** calories per serving

- *250 g (9 oz) dried* ***penne***
- *low fat cooking spray*
- *500 g (1 lb 2 oz)* ***leeks****, trimmed and sliced*
- *40 g (1½ oz) cornflour*
- *600 ml (20 fl oz)* ***skimmed milk***
- *½ vegetable stock cube, crumbled*
- *freshly grated nutmeg*
- *3 tablespoons snipped fresh* ***chives***
- *100 g (3½ oz) Caerphilly cheese, grated*
- *freshly ground black pepper*

Method

1 Preheat the oven to Gas Mark 6/200°C/fan oven 180°C. Bring a large pan of water to the boil, add the pasta and cook according to packet instructions. Drain and rinse in cold water.

2 Meanwhile, heat a lidded, non stick saucepan and spray with the cooking spray. Cook the leeks for 1 minute then add 4 tablespoons of water, cover and cook gently for 5–6 minutes. Tip out on to a plate.

3 Make the sauce in the same saucepan by blending the cornflour with a little of the milk until you have a smooth paste. Gradually blend in the rest of the milk and add the crumbled stock cube. Bring to the boil, stirring, and simmer for 2 minutes. Season with black pepper and nutmeg.

4 Mix the chives and cheese together then stir half into the sauce. Mix with the drained pasta and tip into an ovenproof baking dish. Spoon the leeks on top and scatter the rest of the cheese and chives all over. Bake for 20 minutes until golden brown.

Potato, spinach and cauliflower curry

1½ POINTS VALUE

Adding turmeric to the potatoes and cauliflower is a good idea since it gives them a lovely golden hue.

Serves 4 | **Takes 25** minutes | **6½ *POINTS*** values per recipe | **198** calories per serving

- *low fat cooking spray*
- *1* ***onion****, sliced thinly*
- *2* ***garlic cloves****, crushed*
- *2 tablespoons medium curry powder*
- *1 teaspoon black onion seeds*
- *400 g can chopped* ***tomatoes***
- *200 ml (7 fl oz) hot vegetable stock*
- *500 g (1 lb 2 oz)* ***potatoes****, peeled and diced*
- *400 g (14 oz)* ***cauliflower****, cut into small florets*
- *½ teaspoon ground turmeric (optional)*
- *100 g (3½ oz)* ***young leaf spinach***
- *100 g (3½ fl oz)* ***low fat natural yogurt***

Method

1 Heat a non stick saucepan until hot and spray with the cooking spray. Add the onion and cook for 5 minutes until softened and starting to brown, adding a splash of water if it starts to stick. Add the garlic, curry powder and black onion seeds. Cook for 1 minute, stirring. Mix in the tomatoes and stock and simmer for 5 minutes.

2 Meanwhile, bring a pan of water to the boil and add the potatoes, cauliflower and turmeric, if using. Cook for 6 minutes or until tender. Drain and stir into the curry sauce. Cook gently for 5 minutes.

3 Mix in the spinach and cook until just wilted then marble in the yogurt just before serving.

Cook's tip... This recipe uses black onion seeds, also known as 'kalonji' or 'nigella seeds'. They add a lovely nutty flavour, but if you don't have any, use cumin seeds or brown mustard seeds instead.

1 1/2
POINTS
VALUE

Sausage and apple toad in the hole with onion gravy

This recipe turns the traditional toad in the hole into something really special. It's delicious with French Style Cabbage (on page 152), for an additional ½ ***POINTS*** value per person.

Serves 4 | **Takes 10** minutes to prepare, **40** minutes to cook | **17½ *POINTS*** values per recipe | **333** calories per serving

110 g (4 oz) plain flour
1 egg
300 ml (10 fl oz) skimmed milk
1 tablespoon coarse grain mustard
1 tablespoon finely chopped fresh sage or 1 teaspoon dried sage
low fat cooking spray
8 Quorn Cumberland sausages
2 apples, cored and cut into 8 wedges each
salt and freshly ground black pepper

For the gravy
1 onion, sliced
300 ml (10 fl oz) hot vegetable stock
4 teaspoons vegetarian gravy granules

Method

1 Preheat the oven to Gas Mark 7/220°C/fan oven 200°C. Place a roasting tin, measuring 22 x 30 cm (8½ x 12 inches) and 5 cm (2 inches) deep, in the oven to preheat.

2 Sift the flour into a mixing bowl, break the egg into a well in the centre then gradually mix in the milk until the batter is smooth. Mix in the mustard, sage and seasoning.

3 Remove the roasting tin from the oven, spray it with the cooking spray and add the sausages and apples to the tin. Pour in the batter and bake in the oven for 40 minutes until risen, golden and crisp.

4 To make the gravy, heat a lidded, non stick saucepan and spray with the cooking spray. Cook the onions for 4–5 minutes until well browned then add the vegetable stock. Bring to the boil and simmer, covered, for 20 minutes until very soft. Stir in the gravy granules until thickened then serve with the toad in the hole.

Smart ideas...

Not all vegetables or fruit suit being frozen but green beans, corn, broccoli, carrots, peas, cauliflower and mixed berries do, so try to keep them handy in the freezer.

4 1/2
POINTS
VALUE

Vegetable pad Thai

Serves 2 | Takes 25 minutes | 9½ POINTS values per recipe | 431 calories per serving

- *125 g (4½ oz) dried* rice noodles
- *low fat cooking spray*
- *1 red* onion, *sliced thinly*
- *75 g (2¾ oz)* mange tout, *sliced thinly on the diagonal*
- *75 g (2¾ oz)* baby corn, *sliced thinly on the diagonal*
- *2* garlic cloves, *crushed*
- *1 teaspoon grated root ginger*
- *1 red* chilli, *sliced*
- *125 g (4½ oz)* beansprouts, *rinsed and drained*
- *1* carrot, *peeled and grated coarsely*
- *juice of a lime*
- *1 teaspoon light brown soft sugar*
- *2 tablespoons soy sauce*
- *1* egg, *beaten*
- *3 heaped tablespoons chopped fresh* coriander
- *15 g (½ oz) salted peanuts, chopped finely*

Method

1 Place the noodles in a bowl, cover with boiling water and soak for 4 minutes or until tender. Drain and rinse in cold water.

2 Heat a wok or large frying pan until hot and spray with the cooking spray. Add the onion, mange tout, baby corn and 1 tablespoon of water. Stir fry for 1 minute. Mix in the garlic, ginger and chilli and cook for 1 minute more.

3 Next add the beansprouts, carrot and drained noodles, plus the lime juice, sugar and soy sauce. Toss together for 2 minutes.

4 Drizzle the egg all over the noodle mixture and leave to set for 1 minute then mix in, adding the coriander. Serve scattered with the peanuts.

Ratatouille pasta

The melted Brie topping adds a creamy richness to this tasty dish.

Serves 4 | Takes 30 minutes | 18½ POINTS values per recipe | 332 calories per serving

- *low fat cooking spray*
- *1 red* onion, *chopped roughly*
- *1 red* pepper, *de-seeded and chopped roughly*
- *1 yellow* pepper, *de-seeded and chopped roughly*
- *2* courgettes, *diced*
- *1* aubergine, *diced*
- *3* garlic cloves, *crushed*
- *400 g can chopped* tomatoes
- *200 g (7 oz) dried* fusilli *or* conchiglie
- *100 g (3½ oz) Brie, sliced thinly*
- *freshly ground black pepper*

Method

1 Heat a large, lidded saucepan until hot and spray with the cooking spray. Cook the onion for 2 minutes then add the peppers and cook for 2 minutes more, stirring. Add the courgettes, aubergine and garlic and cook for 3 minutes. Add a splash of water if necessary, to prevent the vegetables from sticking to the pan.

2 Cover the pan and cook for a further 4 minutes over a medium heat until the vegetables have softened then add the tomatoes and simmer for 10 minutes, uncovered. Season with black pepper.

3 Meanwhile, bring a large pan of water to the boil, add the pasta and cook according to the packet instructions, until tender. Preheat the grill.

4 Drain the pasta and mix with the ratatouille. Tip into an ovenproof baking dish and top with the sliced Brie. Grill for 2–3 minutes until the Brie starts to melt. Serve on warm plates.

4 1/2
POINTS
VALUE

Spinach, mushroom and chestnut torte

3 POINTS VALUE

This stunning recipe is ideal for a special occasion. Serve with 150 g (5½ oz) of the Roasted New Potatoes with Shallots (on page 154) per person, for an additional 2 ***POINTS*** values per serving.

Serves 6 | **Takes 25** minutes to prepare, **40** minutes to cook | **16½ *POINTS*** values per recipe | **220** calories per serving

low fat cooking spray
2 onions, sliced
300 g (10½ oz) young leaf spinach
500 g (1 lb 2 oz) chestnut mushrooms, chopped roughly
finely grated zest and juice of ½ a lemon
4 large sheets frozen filo pastry (180 g/6½ oz total), defrosted
15 g (½ oz) dried couscous
200 g (7 oz) cooked chestnuts, chopped roughly
100 g (3½ oz) low fat soft cheese with garlic and herbs

Method

1 Preheat the oven to Gas Mark 4/180°C/fan oven 160°C. Heat a large, lidded saucepan until hot and spray with the cooking spray. Cook the onions for 2 minutes over a high heat until starting to brown. Add 4 tablespoons of water, cover and cook for 5 minutes over a medium heat. Mix in the spinach and cook until wilted then tip into a colander and press out the excess liquid with the back of a spoon. Set aside.

2 Meanwhile, heat a lidded, non stick frying pan until hot, add the mushrooms with the lemon zest and juice and cook for 5 minutes or until tender. Remove the lid and continue to cook until all the juices have evaporated.

3 Cut each sheet of filo into two squares. Spray a 20 cm (8 inch) springform tin with the cooking spray then line with six overlapping squares of the filo to cover the base and sides, with the extra pastry hanging over the rim of the tin. Spray the filo with the cooking spray as you go then place another square of filo in the base of the tin. Sprinkle in the couscous to absorb the cooking juices.

4 Spoon the spinach mixture into the tin then add the mushrooms and chestnuts. Top with small dollops of the soft cheese then place the last square of filo on top. Fold in the overhanging pastry, scrunching up the top, and spray with extra cooking spray.

5 Place on a baking tray and bake for 25 minutes. Remove from the oven and carefully unclip and remove the sides of the tin. Return to the oven and bake for a further 15 minutes until crisp all over. Cut into wedges to serve.

Cook's tip... If you are preparing the torte in advance, make sure that the filling ingredients are completely cool before layering them up in the filo pastry case. Otherwise, the pastry will become soggy.

3
POINTS
VALUE

Cannellini bean and courgette patties

Enjoy this summery tasting combination of courgettes and beans, served with a fresh, light salad.

Ⓥ ❄ Patties only | **Serves 4** | **Takes 30** minutes | **9 *POINTS*** values per recipe | **149** calories per serving

low fat cooking spray
2 **courgettes**, *grated coarsely*
1 bunch **spring onions**, *chopped*
2 **garlic cloves**, *crushed*
1 tablespoon chopped fresh **lemon thyme**
2 x 410 g cans **cannellini beans**, *rinsed and drained*
1 **egg white**, *lightly beaten*
25 g (1 oz) freshly grated Parmesan cheese
freshly ground black pepper

To serve
75 g (2¾ oz) **wild rocket**
4 **tomatoes**, *chopped roughly*
4 teaspoons balsamic vinegar

Method

1 Heat a non stick frying pan until hot and spray with the low fat cooking spray. Squeeze the excess liquid from the courgettes, add to the pan and stir fry with the spring onions, garlic and lemon thyme for 4–5 minutes until wilted and soft.

2 Meanwhile, put the beans, egg white and cheese in a food processor and whizz to a purée. Add the courgette mixture, season with black pepper and mix briefly. Shape into 12 patties, dampening your hands first so that the mixture doesn't stick.

3 Wipe out the frying pan with kitchen paper then spray with the cooking spray. Cook the patties in two batches, for 2½ minutes on each side or until golden and hot.

4 Toss the rocket and tomatoes with the balsamic vinegar and divide between four plates. Serve three patties per person with the salad.

Cook's tip... The patties can be made in advance and kept, covered, in the fridge until ready to cook. If you are planning to freeze the patties, do this before cooking. To keep the individual patties separate when freezing, place on a baking tray in a single layer, cover with clingfilm and freeze until firm. Transfer to a plastic freezer bag and label clearly.

Smart ideas...

Canned pulses make a great storecupboard standby. You can whizz them up for a quick soup, use them in a salad or bulk up casseroles with them. Choose pulses that are packed in water, with no added salt or sugar.

2
POINTS
VALUE

chapter

6 Family favourites

Whether you're after a **warming Sunday feast** or a fabulous family supper, these recipes will be a hit with everyone – Cheesy Turkey Meatloaf and Thatched Beef Pie are especially good crowd pleasers. There are **healthier versions** of favourites too such as the Crispy Garlic Chicken Breasts. What's more, the recipes are all good value and kind to the budget.

Rosemary roast chicken on page 102

Thatched beef pie

This makes a pleasant change from cottage pie but it is still very family friendly. It can easily be prepared earlier in the day, ready to pop in the oven at tea time.

Serves 6 | **Takes 30** minutes to prepare, **25** minutes to cook | **35 *POINTS*** values per recipe | **326** calories per serving

low fat cooking spray
500 g (1 lb 2 oz) **extra lean minced beef**
1 **onion**, *chopped finely*
1 tablespoon plain flour
300 ml (10 fl oz) hot beef stock
a few shakes of Worcestershire sauce
415 g can **reduced sugar and salt baked beans**
freshly ground black pepper

For the thatch topping
900 g (2 lb) **potatoes**, *whole, unpeeled and all the same size (medium)*
3 **carrots**, *peeled and grated coarsely*
40 g (1½ oz) low fat mature cheese, grated

Method

1 Preheat the oven to Gas Mark 5/190°C/fan oven 170°C.

2 Heat a large, lidded, non stick saucepan until hot and spray with the cooking spray. Add the minced beef and onion and cook for 5 minutes over a high heat, stirring to break up. Add the flour, followed by the stock and stir. Season with black pepper and add a few shakes of Worcestershire sauce. Cover and simmer gently for 15 minutes and then stir in the baked beans.

3 Meanwhile, bring a lidded saucepan of water to the boil, add the potatoes and cook for 12 minutes.

4 Heat a non stick frying pan and spray with the low fat cooking spray. Add the carrots and stir fry for 3–4 minutes until softened. Tip into a mixing bowl.

5 Drain the potatoes, cover with cold water and cool for 2 minutes. Drain and then scrape off the skins using a table knife. Grate coarsely and add to the carrots, using two forks to mix together.

6 Tip the mince and beans into a large ovenproof baking dish. Spoon the potato and carrot topping on top and sprinkle with the cheese. Bake for 25 minutes until the topping is golden and crisp.

Why not try... a vegetarian version of this dish by replacing the minced beef with Quorn mince. Add the Quorn mince in step 2 with the flour. Use vegetable stock instead of beef stock and omit the Worcestershire sauce. This will be 4 ***POINTS*** values per serving.

Cook's tip... Make sure you use medium potatoes and leave them whole. Cutting large potatoes in half doesn't work well since, once cut, the potatoes don't hold together well enough for grating.

6
POINTS
VALUE

Roast beef with onion Yorkshire pudding

A classic Sunday roast is always a crowd pleaser. Adding some onions to the Yorkshire pudding makes it even more delicious.

Serves 6 | **Takes 20** minutes to prepare, **1½–1¾** hours to cook | **42½ *POINTS*** values per recipe | **335** calories per serving

1 kg (2 lb 4 oz) topside of beef
1 teaspoon dry mustard (optional)
150 ml (5 fl oz) red wine
500 ml (18 fl oz) hot beef stock
15 g (½ oz) cornflour
salt and freshly ground black pepper

For the onion Yorkshire pudding
125 g (4½ oz) plain flour
1 egg
300 ml (10 fl oz) skimmed milk
low fat cooking spray
1 large onion*, sliced thickly*
salt and freshly ground black pepper

Method

1 Remove the beef from the fridge 30 minutes before cooking. Preheat the oven to Gas Mark 5/190°C/fan oven 170°C.

2 Season the beef and rub with the mustard, if using. Place in a roasting tin and roast in the oven for 1 hour for medium cooked beef. If you prefer it well done, give it an extra 15 minutes.

3 Meanwhile, make up the Yorkshire pudding batter by sifting the flour into a bowl with a pinch of salt and then gradually beat in the egg and milk to give a smooth batter. Season and set aside. Spray a roasting tin with the cooking spray and add the sliced onion.

4 When the hour is up, drain off any fat from around the beef joint, pour in the red wine and return to the oven for 5 minutes. At the same time, place the tin holding the onions in the oven above the beef for 5 minutes.

5 Remove the beef to a carving dish to rest, covered loosely with foil. Increase the oven temperature to Gas Mark 7/220°C/fan oven 200°C and cook the onions for another 5 minutes. Pour the batter into the tin with the onions and cook in the top half of the oven for 25–30 minutes until well risen and crisp.

6 To make the gravy, pour the stock into the beef roasting tin, place on the hob using oven gloves to hold the tin and bubble for 5 minutes, scraping the bottom with a wooden spoon to release the delicious caramelised bits from the tin. Mix the cornflour to a paste with a little cold water then pour into the tin and stir until thickened. Simmer for a couple of minutes and then pour into a warmed jug or pan.

7 Carve the beef and serve three medium slices (115 g/4¼ oz) of beef per person with a portion of onion Yorkshire pudding and gravy.

7
POINTS
VALUE

Cranberry glazed gammon with colcannon

(12)

6 *POINTS* VALUE

Simmering the gammon in cranberry juice before glazing and roasting makes the meat beautifully moist and flavoursome. Serve with Chantenay carrots and runner beans, for no extra *POINTS* values.

Serves 6 | **Takes 15** minutes to prepare, **1¾** hours to cook | **35½ *POINTS*** values per recipe | **450** calories per serving

750 g (1 lb 10 oz) **smoked gammon** *joint, rinsed*
1 litre (1¾ pints) no added sugar cranberry juice
1 **onion***, quartered*
12 whole cloves
75 g (2¾ oz) cranberry sauce
¼ teaspoon ground ginger

For the colcannon

1.25 kg (2 lb 12 oz) **potatoes***, peeled and cut into chunks*
low fat cooking spray
2 **leeks***, sliced*
½ **Savoy cabbage***, shredded*
100 ml (3½ fl oz) **skimmed milk**
freshly grated nutmeg
freshly ground black pepper

Method

1 Place the gammon in a deep, lidded saucepan that will hold it snugly and pour in the cranberry juice. Add extra water to cover the gammon if necessary. Add the onion and cloves, cover the pan and bring to the boil. Simmer, partially covered, for 1 hour.

2 Preheat the oven to Gas Mark 6/200°C/fan oven 180°C. Drain the gammon and remove any casing or binding. Trim off any skin and fat then sit the joint in a foil-lined roasting tin. Mix the cranberry sauce and ginger together and spoon over the gammon. Roast in the oven for 20 minutes and then rest for 10 minutes, loosely covered with foil.

3 While the gammon is roasting, bring a pan of water to the boil and cook the potatoes until tender.

4 Spray a separate, lidded, non stick saucepan with the cooking spray and cook the leeks for 1 minute. Add 2 tablespoons of water and cook, covered, for 2 minutes. Stir in the cabbage and 6 tablespoons of water. Replace the lid and cook for 5 minutes, stirring once or twice. Drain off any excess liquid.

5 Drain the potatoes in a colander. Heat the milk in the same saucepan used for the potatoes then return the potatoes to the pan and mash with the milk. Season and add the nutmeg. Stir in the leeks and cabbage.

6 Slice the gammon thinly and serve one-sixth of the joint per person with the colcannon.

Smart ideas...

Make a shopping list before you go to the supermarket – and stick to it. Check what you've already got in the fridge and store cupboard so you don't buy what you already have. You'll spend less and avoid temptation.

6
POINTS
VALUE

Penne with lamb ragu

7½ POINTS VALUE

A twist on spaghetti Bolognese, this lamb version is seasoned with a touch of mint and cinnamon, giving it a slightly Greek flavour.

❄ Ragu sauce only | **Serves 6** | **Takes 15** minutes to prepare, **45** minutes to cook | **45½ *POINTS*** values per recipe | **376** calories per serving

low fat cooking spray
500 g (1 lb 2 oz) **lean lamb mince**
2 **onions,** *chopped finely*
3 **garlic cloves**, *crushed*
2 teaspoons dried **mint**
½ teaspoon ground cinnamon
2 x 400 g cans chopped **tomatoes**
350 g (12 oz) dried **penne**
salt and freshly ground black pepper

Method

1 Heat a lidded, flameproof casserole dish on the hob and spray with the cooking spray. Add the lamb mince and the onions and cook for 5 minutes, stirring frequently to break up the mince.
2 Add the garlic, mint and cinnamon to the casserole and cook for 1 minute before stirring in the tomatoes and seasoning. Bring to a simmer, cover and cook gently for 45 minutes.
3 Around 20 minutes before the sauce is ready, bring a saucepan of water to the boil and cook the pasta according to packet instructions. Drain and toss with the ragu sauce. Serve immediately.

Why not try... replacing the minced lamb with Quorn mince for a vegetarian version, for 4 ***POINTS*** values per serving. Quorn doesn't need to be browned so add it in step 2 with the garlic, mint and cinnamon.

Roasted sausage and pepper rigatoni

7½ POINTS VALUE

Here is a deliciously different take on pasta, with a roasted vegetable and sausage sauce.

Serves 4 | **Takes 10** minutes to prepare, **30** minutes to cook | **29½ *POINTS*** values per recipe | **433** calories per serving

454 g pack low fat sausages
1 red **pepper,** *de-seeded and chopped roughly*
1 yellow **pepper**, *de-seeded and chopped roughly*
3 **garlic cloves**, *crushed*
a pinch of dried chillies
low fat cooking spray
350 g (12 oz) **cherry tomatoes**, *halved*
250 g (9 oz) dried **rigatoni**
2 heaped tablespoons shredded fresh **basil**

Method

1 Preheat the oven to Gas Mark 7/220°C/fan oven 200°C.
2 Snip the sausages into chunks using kitchen scissors and toss together with the peppers, garlic and chillies in a large roasting tin. Spray with the cooking spray and roast for 15 minutes
3 Stir the cherry tomatoes into the roasting tin and cook for a further 10–15 minutes.
4 Meanwhile, bring a pan of water to the boil and cook the pasta according to the packet instructions. Drain thoroughly.
5 Add the pasta to the roasted sausage and pepper mixture and stir in the fresh basil. Serve immediately.

Why not try... swapping Quorn Cumberland sausages for the pork sausages? This will be 5 ***POINTS*** values per serving.

7 1/2
POINTS
VALUE

Rosemary roast chicken

Roasting the chicken breast-side down helps to keep the breast meat moist.

Serves 4 | **Takes 15** minutes to prepare, **1¼** hours to cook + **15** minutes resting | **23 *POINTS*** values per recipe | **282** calories per serving

1.75 kg (3 lb 14 oz) whole chicken
1 lemon, halved; juice squeezed into a bowl
2 fresh rosemary sprigs plus 1 tablespoon chopped fresh rosemary
low fat cooking spray
500 g (1 lb 2 oz) new potatoes, halved
350 g (12 oz) Chantenay carrots, trimmed
3 leeks, trimmed and each cut into 6 chunks
salt and freshly ground black pepper

Method

1 Preheat the oven to Gas Mark 6/200°C/fan oven 180°C. Wipe the chicken inside and out with kitchen paper. Tuck the squeezed lemon halves and rosemary sprigs inside the chicken cavity. Season the chicken and spray with the cooking spray. Sit in a large roasting tin, breast side down. Roast for 30 minutes.

2 Toss together the potatoes, carrots and leeks and spray with the cooking spray. Add to the roasting tin around the chicken. Roast for 30 minutes, stirring the vegetables halfway through.

3 Turn the chicken breast side up and pour the lemon juice over the chicken and vegetables. Scatter with the rosemary, stir the vegetables again and return to the oven for 15 minutes.

4 Remove the chicken from the oven and let it rest for 15 minutes, loosely covered with foil. Transfer the vegetables to a dish and keep warm. Remove the skin and carve the chicken to serve four 45 g (1½ oz) slices per person, with the vegetables.

Cheesy turkey meatloaf

This meatloaf is delicious served with runner beans and mashed potato (200 g/7 oz potatoes, mashed with 2 tablespoons of skimmed milk per person), for an extra 2½ *POINTS* values per serving.

Serves 4 | **Takes 10** minutes to prepare, **30** minutes to cook | **18 *POINTS*** values per recipe | **340** calories per serving

2 medium slices bread, torn roughly
1 onion, chopped roughly
1 courgette, grated coarsely
500 g (1 lb 2 oz) turkey mince
1 tablespoon fresh thyme leaves, plus extra to garnish
2 tablespoons tomato ketchup
75 g (2¾ oz) low fat mature cheese, grated
300 g (10½ oz) cherry tomatoes on the vine
salt and freshly ground black pepper

Method

1 Preheat the oven to Gas Mark 6/200°C/fan oven 180°C. Add the bread and onion to a food processor and whizz until finely chopped. Tip into a mixing bowl.

2 Squeeze the excess liquid from the courgette and then add to the bowl, along with the turkey mince, thyme, ketchup and half the cheese. Add seasoning and mix well. Shape the mixture into a loaf around 8 x 20 cm (3¼ x 8 inches) and place in a roasting tin. Bake in the oven for 20 minutes.

3 Snip the vine tomatoes into small clusters and arrange around the meatloaf. Baste with the juices in the tin. Cook for 5 minutes and then scatter the remaining cheese over the meatloaf. Cook for a final 5 minutes.

4 Slice the meatloaf and serve with the roasted tomatoes and a sprinkling of fresh thyme leaves.

4 1/2
POINTS
VALUE

Roast lamb with fruity herb stuffing

Serves 4 | **Takes 20** minutes to prepare, **1½–1¾** hours to cook + **10–15** minutes resting | **18½ *POINTS*** values per recipe | **312** calories per serving

- *low fat cooking spray*
- *1 small* **onion**, *chopped finely*
- *1* **egg white**, *lightly beaten*
- *60 g (2 oz) fresh breadcrumbs*
- *40 g (1½ oz) ready to eat semi-dried apricots, diced*
- *2 heaped tablespoons chopped fresh* **parsley**
- *1 tablespoon chopped fresh lemon* **thyme**
- *finely grated zest and juice of ½ a lemon*
- *650 g (1 lb 7 oz) boneless* **lamb leg** *joint, trimmed of all fat*
- *freshly ground black pepper*

Method

1 Preheat the oven to Gas Mark 5/190°C/fan oven 170°C. Heat a lidded non stick saucepan until hot and spray with the cooking spray. Add the onion with 4 tablespoons of water. Cover and cook for 5 minutes over a medium heat until softened.

2 Meanwhile, make the stuffing. Mix the egg white with the breadcrumbs, apricots, herbs, lemon zest and juice and season. Add the cooked onion.

3 Unroll the lamb on a chopping board so that it lies flat. Carefully slice through the lamb from the centre towards the sides, opening out the lamb horizontally like the jacket cover of a book.

4 Press the stuffing on to the lamb joint then re-roll and secure with string in three or four places. Place in a roasting tin, season and cover loosely with foil. Roast for 1¼ hours for slightly pink lamb, or for 1½ hours for well done. Remove the foil and roast for a final 15 minutes to brown the joint. Rest for 10–15 minutes before carving into slices. Serve three medium slices of stuffed lamb per person.

Crispy garlic chicken breasts

This is delicious served with 150 g (5½ oz) new potatoes per person for an additional 1½ *POINTS* values per serving, plus your favourite zero *POINTS* value green vegetable.

Serves 4 | **Takes 15** minutes to prepare, **20** minutes to cook | **13½ *POINTS*** values per recipe | **246** calories per serving

- *2* **garlic cloves**, *crushed*
- *1 tablespoon finely chopped fresh* **parsley**
- *75 g (2¾ oz)* **low fat soft cheese**
- *4 x 125 g (4½ oz)* **skinless boneless chicken breasts**
- *1* **egg**
- *1 tablespoon* **skimmed milk**
- *75 g (2¾ oz) fresh breadcrumbs*
- *low fat cooking spray*
- *freshly ground black pepper*

Method

1 Preheat the oven to Gas Mark 6/200°C/fan oven 180°C.

2 In a bowl, mix together the garlic and parsley with the soft cheese and black pepper. Cut a deep pocket in each chicken breast, taking care not to cut right through, then stuff the soft cheese mixture inside, closing the flesh around the stuffing as far as possible.

3 Beat the egg with the milk in a shallow dish, and spread the breadcrumbs out on a plate.

4 Dip each chicken breast first in the egg mixture and then in crumbs to coat all over. Place on a non stick baking tray and spray with the cooking spray. Bake for 20 minutes until crisp and cooked through.

3 1/2
POINTS
VALUE

Spanish vegetable rice

Serves 4 | **Takes 15** minutes to prepare, **20** minutes to cook | **15 *POINTS*** values per recipe | **313** calories per serving

low fat cooking spray
1 ***onion****, chopped finely*
1 red ***pepper****, de-seeded and sliced*
1 yellow ***pepper****, de-seeded and sliced*
200 g (7 oz) ***button mushrooms****, halved*
3 ***tomatoes****, chopped roughly*
250 g (9 oz) paella or risotto rice
850 ml (1½ pints) hot vegetable stock
1 pinch saffron (optional)
200 g (7 oz) frozen ***peas***
juice of ½ a lemon
2 heaped tablespoons chopped fresh ***parsley***
salt and freshly ground black pepper

Method

1 Place a large, lidded saucepan on the hob and spray with the cooking spray. Add the onion with 2 tablespoons of water and cook for 4 minutes. Stir in the peppers and cook for a further 2 minutes.

2 Add the mushrooms and tomatoes and cook for 2 minutes or until the tomatoes start to soften. Mix in the rice and cook, stirring, for 1 minute.

3 Pour in 700 ml (1¼ pints) stock, add the saffron, if using, and bring to the boil. Season, cover and simmer gently for 15 minutes until the rice is almost tender and most of the stock has been absorbed.

4 Add the peas and the remaining stock to the pan and cook, uncovered, for 5 minutes. Stir in the lemon juice and parsley just before serving.

Why not try... stirring in 250 g (9 oz) cooked, peeled prawns with the peas, for 5 ***POINTS*** values per person.

Tuna and sweetcorn rosti cake

Serves 4 | **Takes 45** minutes | **17½ *POINTS*** values per recipe | **294** calories per serving

750 g (1 lb 10 oz) floury or waxy ***potatoes****, unpeeled and left whole*
low fat cooking spray
1 large ***onion****, sliced thinly*
150 g (5½ oz) frozen ***sweetcorn***
2 x 200 g cans ***tuna in spring water****, drained*
1 tablespoon sunflower oil
salt and freshly ground black pepper

Method

1 Bring a lidded pan of water to the boil and add the potatoes. Cover and cook for 12 minutes. Drain then cover with cold water and cool for 2 minutes. Drain again and when cool enough to handle, scrape off the skins using a table knife. Coarsely grate the potatoes into a bowl.

2 Meanwhile, spray a lidded, non stick frying pan with the cooking spray and cook the onion for 3–4 minutes until starting to colour. Add 6 tablespoons of water to the pan. Cover and cook gently for 5 minutes until the onions are softened and the liquid has evaporated.

3 Place the sweetcorn in a bowl, cover with boiling water and leave to defrost for 2 minutes then drain.

4 Using a couple of forks, mix the onion, sweetcorn and tuna into the grated potato. Heat half the oil in a non stick frying pan then add the rosti mixture to make one large rosti, pressing down firmly. Cook for 7 minutes over a medium heat.

5 Slide the rosti on to a plate. Add the remaining oil to the frying pan. Upturn the plate over the frying pan to cook the other side of the rosti for a further 7 minutes. Cut into four wedges and serve.

Why not try... replacing the tuna with a 418 g can of red salmon, for 5½ ***POINTS*** values per serving.

4 1/2
POINTS
VALUE

Mediterranean cod bake

Serve with 60 g (2 oz) dried tagliatelle per person, cooked according to the packet instructions, for an extra 3 *POINTS* values per serving, as well as some broccoli spears.

Serves 4 | **Takes 15** minutes to prepare, **15** minutes to cook | **15 *POINTS*** values per recipe | **289** calories per serving

low fat cooking spray
1 yellow pepper, de-seeded and sliced
1 green pepper, de-seeded and sliced
2 garlic cloves, sliced
400 g can chopped tomatoes
3 heaped tablespoons shredded fresh basil
4 x 125 g (4½ oz) skinless cod fillets
125 g (4½ oz) reduced fat mozzarella, torn
freshly ground black pepper

Method

1 Preheat the oven to Gas Mark 6/200°C/fan oven 180°C. Lightly spray a baking dish with the cooking spray.

2 Heat a non stick frying pan until hot, spray with the cooking spray and cook the peppers and garlic for 4 minutes until browned and starting to soften. Add the tomatoes, basil, season with black pepper, then simmer for 3–4 minutes until slightly thickened.

3 Place the cod fillets in the baking dish and pour the sauce over the fish. Scatter the mozzarella over the top and bake for 15 minutes.

Why not try... other white fish fillets such as hoki or pollock instead of cod for the same *POINTS* values – they are often better value than cod and just as tasty.

Cheese and tomato bread pudding

5 *POINTS* VALUE

This is a wonderful way to use up leftover bread and it's a cheap and filling family meal.

Serves 4 | **Takes 10** minutes to prepare, **35** minutes to cook | **19 *POINTS*** values per recipe | **313** calories per serving

low fat cooking spray
400 g can chopped tomatoes
2 tablespoons chopped fresh thyme or
1 teaspoon dried thyme
100 g (3½ oz) low fat mature cheese, grated
4 eggs
400 ml (14 fl oz) skimmed milk
150 g (5½ oz) day old French bread, sliced thinly
salt and freshly ground black pepper

Method

1 Preheat the oven to Gas Mark 4/180°C/fan oven 160°C. Lightly spray an ovenproof dish with the cooking spray.

2 Mix the tomatoes with half of the thyme, then spoon half of the tomatoes into the base of the dish and scatter with about a quarter of the cheese.

3 In a large bowl, beat the eggs with milk and seasoning. Dip the slices of bread in the eggy mixture, letting them soak in it briefly. Arrange the bread slices on top of the tomatoes and cheese, overlapping slightly.

4 Spoon on the rest of the tomatoes and scatter with the remaining cheese and thyme. Pour the remaining egg mixture all over the dish. Cover with foil and bake for 20 minutes.

5 Remove the foil. Bake for a further 15 minutes until the mixture is puffed up and golden brown on top.

5
POINTS
VALUE

Stuffed mushrooms

The sunflower seeds in this colourful dish add a pleasant crunch which makes a nice contrast to the tender juiciness of the mushrooms.

Serves 2 | **Takes 15** minutes to prepare, **10** minutes to cook | **8½ *POINTS*** values per recipe | **307** calories per serving

4 large flat **mushrooms***, stalks removed*
low fat cooking spray
125 ml (4 fl oz) hot vegetable stock
75 g (2¾ oz) dried **couscous**
75 g (2¾ oz) frozen **sweetcorn** *or tinned sweetcorn, drained*
12 **cherry tomatoes***, halved*
15 g (½ oz) sunflower seeds
40 g (1½ oz) low fat mature cheese, grated finely

Method

1 Preheat the oven to Gas Mark 6/200°C/fan oven 180°C.

2 Spray the mushrooms with the cooking spray and season with black pepper. Place on a baking tray, open cup side down, and cook in the oven for 8 minutes.

3 Meanwhile, pour the hot stock over the couscous in a bowl. Cover with a plate and leave to stand for 6–7 minutes to soften. If using frozen sweetcorn, bring a small saucepan of water to the boil and cook the sweetcorn for 2–3 minutes then drain.

4 Add the sweetcorn, tomatoes and half the sunflower seeds to the couscous and mix together. Remove the mushrooms from the oven and flip them over. Pile the couscous on the mushrooms and top with the cheese and the rest of the sunflower seeds.

5 Return to the oven for 10 minutes until the cheese is melted and golden.

Smart ideas...

Grate hard cheeses such as low fat mature cheese or Parmesan cheese and store them in a food bag in the freezer, ready to use from frozen. You can then easily measure out just what you need.

4 1/2
POINTS
VALUE

chapter 7

Comfort food

These comforting meals require very little preparation but the result is **so satisfying**. Just let them simmer away while you put your feet up or get on with something else. You'll love the Sausage and Potato Hotpot and Minced Beef and Dumplings. Tasty variations of **well-loved dishes** such as Smoked Haddock Macaroni Cheese are sure to become favourites too.

Spicy Meatballs on page 124

Mediterranean chicken stew

This succulent chicken and vegetable stew is bursting with flavour. Serve with steamed broccoli florets, for no additional *POINTS* values.

Serves 6 | **Takes 25** minutes to prepare, **35** minutes to cook | **33 *POINTS* values per recipe** | **273** calories per serving

low fat cooking spray
*1 **onion**, sliced finely*
*3 **celery** sticks, sliced*
*500 g (1 lb 2 oz) **skinless boneless chicken thighs**, diced*
*3 **garlic cloves**, sliced*
*1 yellow **pepper**, de-seeded and sliced*
150 ml (5 fl oz) white wine
½ an orange
*400 g can chopped **tomatoes***
a small pinch of saffron threads
600 ml (20 fl oz) hot chicken stock
*750 g (1 lb 10 oz) small **new potatoes**, halved*
2 tablespoons cornflour
freshly ground black pepper

Method

1 Heat a lidded, flameproof casserole dish on the hob and spray with the cooking spray. Add the onion and celery and cook for 5 minutes until softened.

2 Meanwhile, heat a non stick frying pan until hot and spray with the cooking spray. Brown the chicken for about 5 minutes.

3 Add the garlic and peppers to the casserole and cook for 1 minute, stirring. Pour in the wine. Pare a few strips of zest from the orange using a vegetable peeler and add to the casserole. Squeeze the juice out of the orange half and add it to the casserole. Boil rapidly for 2 minutes then add the tomatoes, saffron, stock, potatoes and browned chicken. Season with black pepper and bring to the boil. Cover and simmer for 35 minutes.

4 Blend the cornflour with a little cold water and stir into the casserole until the sauce has thickened. Serve in deep plates to hold the sauce.

Why not try... the same weight of skinless boneless chicken breast fillets in this recipe, for 3½ ***POINTS*** values per serving.

5 1/2
POINTS
VALUE

Caribbean chicken casserole

This spicy casserole is packed with colourful vegetables and pulses.

Serves 2 | **Takes 15** minutes to prepare, **25** minutes to cook | **8 *POINTS*** values per recipe | **319** calories per serving

low fat cooking spray
200 g (7 oz) **skinless boneless chicken breast**, *diced*
½ orange **pepper**, *de-seeded and chopped roughly*
2 teaspoons Caribbean seasoning
200 g (7 oz) **sweet potato**, *peeled and diced*
½ x 410g can **black eyed beans**, *rinsed and drained*
2 **tomatoes**, *cut into wedges*
200 ml (7 fl oz) hot chicken stock
50 g (1¾ oz) frozen **sweetcorn**
freshly ground black pepper

Method

1 Heat a lidded saucepan until hot and spray with the cooking spray. Add the chicken and pepper and brown for 4 minutes. Add the Caribbean seasoning and sweet potato and cook for 1 minute, stirring.
2 Mix in the black eyed beans, tomatoes and stock. Cover and simmer for 20 minutes then add the sweetcorn and cook for a further 5 minutes.

Minced beef and dumplings

The dumplings make this deliciously satisfying.

❄ Mince casserole only | **Serves 4** | **Takes 20** minutes to prepare, **40** minutes to cook | **28 *POINTS*** values per recipe | **378** calories per serving

low fat cooking spray
500 g (1 lb 2 oz) **extra lean minced beef**
1 **onion**, *chopped*
2 **carrots**, *peeled and diced*
200 g (7 oz) **swede**, *diced*
200 g (7 oz) **mushrooms**, *chopped*
25 g (1 oz) plain flour
425 ml (15 fl oz) hot beef stock
a few shakes of Worcestershire sauce

For the dumplings
110 g (4 oz) self raising flour
50 g (1¾ oz) low fat spread
1 tablespoon coarse grain mustard
½ tablespoon chopped fresh **thyme**
salt and freshly ground black pepper

Method

1 Heat a lidded, flameproof casserole on the hob and spray with the cooking spray. Add the mince and onion and brown for 5 minutes, stirring to break up the mince. Add the carrots, swede and mushrooms and cook for 2 minutes.
2 Stir in the flour followed by the stock and Worcestershire sauce. Cover and simmer for 20 minutes.
3 To make the dumplings, sift the flour into a mixing bowl. Rub in the low fat spread then stir in the mustard, thyme and seasoning. Add just enough cold water to make a soft but not sticky dough.
4 Shape into eight dumplings and add to the casserole. Replace the lid and cook for 20 minutes until the dumplings are fluffy and puffed up.

7
POINTS
VALUE

Persian lamb pilaff

Serve this fragrant pilaff with lightly cooked green beans, for no additional ***POINTS*** values.

Serves 4 | **Takes 15** minutes to prepare, **45** minutes to cook | **22½ *POINTS*** values per recipe | **374** calories per serving

low fat cooking spray
350 g (12 oz) lean lamb leg steaks, trimmed of all fat and diced
1 large onion, chopped
1 teaspoon ground cinnamon
175 g (6 oz) dried brown basmati rice
425 ml (15 fl oz) boiling water
50 g (1¾ oz) dried sour cherries
juice of ½ a lemon
150 g (5½ oz) frozen peas
25 g (1 oz) unsalted pistachios, chopped finely, to serve

Method

1 Heat a lidded, flameproof casserole on the hob and spray with the cooking spray. Add the lamb and brown for about 5 minutes then transfer to a plate. You may need to do this in batches. Add the onion to the casserole and cook for 3 minutes until starting to colour at the edges. Return the lamb to the casserole, adding any juices from the plate.
2 Stir in the cinnamon and rice, then add the boiling water, sour cherries and lemon juice. Bring to the boil, stir well and cover tightly. Reduce the heat to low and cook, undisturbed, for 40 minutes.
3 Mix the peas into the pilaff and cook for a further 5 minutes. Scatter with the pistachios to serve.

Why not try... using white basmati rice. It will only need to be cooked for 15 minutes in step 2. The ***POINTS*** values remain the same.

Hearty turkey casserole

Serve with 200 g (7 oz) potatoes, mashed with 2 tablespoons of skimmed milk per person, for an extra 2½ ***POINTS*** values per serving.

Serves 4 | **Takes 15** minutes to prepare, **30** minutes to cook | **15 *POINTS*** values per recipe | **293** calories per serving

low fat cooking spray
500 g (1 lb 2 oz) turkey breast, diced
2 large leeks, sliced thickly
400 g (14 oz) butternut squash, peeled, de-seeded and chopped roughly
2 tablespoons plain flour
425 ml (15 fl oz) hot chicken stock
40 g (1½ oz) dried Puy lentils, rinsed
1 teaspoon dried tarragon or 1 tablespoon chopped fresh tarragon
2 tablespoons half fat crème fraîche
freshly ground black pepper

Method

1 Heat a lidded, flameproof casserole on the hob and spray with the cooking spray. Season the turkey with black pepper, add to the casserole and brown for 4 minutes, stirring occasionally. This may need to be done in batches.
2 Add the leeks to the casserole and cook for 2 minutes then stir in the butternut squash and flour, mixing well to coat. Gradually blend in the stock and mix in the Puy lentils and tarragon. Bring to a simmer, cover and cook gently for 30 minutes until tender.
3 Stir in the crème fraîche just before serving.

Why not try... using the same weight of diced, skinless, boneless chicken breast, for 3½ ***POINTS*** values per serving.

4
POINTS
VALUE

Slow cooked beef and pasta casserole

A richly flavoured and filling casserole.

End of step 4, after cooling | **Serves 6** | **Takes 20** minutes to prepare, **1¾** hours to cook | **33 *POINTS*** values per recipe | **385** calories per serving

low fat cooking spray
750 g (1 lb 10 oz) **lean beef casserole steak**, *diced*
1 large **onion**, *sliced*
3 **lean back bacon** *rashers, chopped*
4 **garlic cloves**, *crushed*
700 g jar **passata** *with basil*
18 pitted **black olives in brine**, *drained*
600 ml (20 fl oz) hot beef stock
300 g (10½ oz) **mushrooms**, *chopped roughly*
225 g (8 oz) dried **fusilli** *or* **penne**
freshly ground black pepper

Method

1 Preheat the oven to Gas Mark 1/140°C/fan oven 120°C. Heat a large, non stick frying pan until hot and spray with the cooking spray. Season the beef, brown in two batches and then remove to a plate.

2 Meanwhile, heat a lidded, flameproof casserole on the hob and spray with the cooking spray. Add the onion and cook for 3–4 minutes. Add the bacon and garlic and cook for 2 minutes then stir in the beef, passata and olives.

3 Use a little of the stock to deglaze the frying pan, stirring, then pour this liquid and the rest of the stock in to the casserole. Bring to a simmer, cover and transfer to the oven for 1¼ hours.

4 When the time is up, stir in the mushrooms and cook for a further 15 minutes.

5 Finally, add the pasta, pushing it into the sauce. Cover and cook in the oven for 15–20 minutes until the beef is tender and the pasta is cooked.

Moroccan Quorn mince

The Jewelled Couscous (on page 154) makes an ideal accompaniment to this recipe, for 3½ *POINTS* values per serving.

Serves 4 | **Takes 25** minutes | **10½ *POINTS*** values per recipe | **195** calories per serving

low fat cooking spray
1 red **onion**, *chopped*
½ teaspoon ground cinnamon
1 teaspoon ground cumin
350 g (12 oz) **Quorn mince**
1 tablespoon plain flour
450 ml (16 fl oz) hot vegetable stock
finely grated zest and juice of ½ a lemon
410 g can **chick peas**, *rinsed and drained*
4 heaped tablespoons roughly chopped fresh **coriander**

Method

1 Heat a lidded, flameproof casserole on the hob and spray with the cooking spray. Add the onion and cook for 3 minutes then add the spices, Quorn mince and flour and cook for 1 minute, stirring.

2 Add the stock, lemon zest and juice, as well as the chick peas. Bring to the boil, cover and simmer for 12 minutes. Add the coriander before serving.

Why not try... replacing the Quorn mince with the same quantity of lean minced lamb and following the same instructions, for meat lovers – it's only 5½ ***POINTS*** values per person.

2 1/2
POINTS
VALUE

Summery pork mince

Lean mince is very practical for family meals, but it's easy to get stuck in a rut, cooking the same few dishes. This citrusy mince sauce has a delightfully fresh flavour, and can also be served tossed through spaghetti (250 g/9 oz dried weight for four people) instead of with rice, for the same *POINTS* values per serving.

❄ End of step 2, after cooling | **Serves 4** | **Takes 15** minutes to prepare, **35** minutes to cook | **24½ *POINTS*** values per recipe | **455** calories per serving

low fat cooking spray
500 g (1 lb 2 oz) **lean pork mince**
2 **carrots***, peeled and grated coarsely*
1 **courgette***, grated coarsely*
2 **garlic cloves***, crushed*
2 tablespoons chopped fresh **lemon thyme**
finely grated zest and juice of a lemon
15 g (½ oz) plain flour
400 ml (14 fl oz) hot chicken stock
250 g (9 oz) **brown basmati rice**
600 ml (20 fl oz) boiling water
150 g (5½ oz) **fine green beans**

Method

1 Heat a lidded, flameproof casserole on the hob and spray with the cooking spray. Add the pork mince and brown for 5 minutes, stirring to break it up. Add the carrots, courgette, garlic and thyme, plus the lemon zest. Cook for 2 minutes, stirring.

2 Add the flour, half the lemon juice and the stock. Bring to a simmer, cover and cook for 20 minutes.

3 Meanwhile, place the rice, boiling water and the rest of the lemon juice in a large, lidded saucepan and bring to the boil. Stir once then cover and reduce the heat to the lowest setting. Cook undisturbed for 25 minutes until the rice is tender and the liquid has been absorbed.

4 Add the green beans to the casserole and replace the lid. Cook for 10 minutes until tender. Serve ladled over the lemon rice.

Smart ideas...

Make large batches of recipes like bolognese sauce, chilli and casseroles, then freeze portions ready for an easy low ***POINTS*** value meal when you don't have the time or inclination to cook.

6
POINTS
VALUE

Spicy meatballs

The Spiced Brown Rice and Mushroom Pilau (on page 156) is fabulous with this curry, for an extra 2½ **POINTS** values per serving.

❄ **Serves 4** | **Takes 20** minutes to prepare, **30** minutes to cook | **23 POINTS** values per recipe | **262** calories per serving

low fat cooking spray
1 large onion, chopped finely
1 garlic clove, crushed
1 teaspoon ground cumin
1 tablespoon medium curry powder
400 g can chopped tomatoes
300 ml (10 fl oz) hot beef stock
75 g (2¾ oz) fresh wholemeal breadcrumbs
2 tablespoons skimmed milk
1 teaspoon ground cumin
500 g (1 lb 2 oz) lean beef mince
1 tablespoon chopped fresh coriander (optional), plus extra to serve
freshly ground black pepper

Method

1 For the sauce, heat a lidded, flameproof casserole on the hob and spray with the cooking spray. Add the onion, cook for 4 minutes then add the garlic, cumin and curry powder. Cook for 1 minute, stirring. Add the tomatoes and stock, bring to the boil and simmer briskly, uncovered, for 10 minutes.

2 Meanwhile, mix the breadcrumbs and milk in a bowl then add the cumin, minced beef and coriander, if using, and season with black pepper. Shape the mixture into 24 meatballs. Heat a large, non stick frying pan and spray with the cooking spray. Add the meatballs and brown for about 5 minutes, turning to colour evenly.

3 Add the meatballs to the curry sauce and simmer, partially covered, for 30 minutes. Serve topped with extra coriander, if you wish.

Smoked haddock macaroni cheese

Adding smoked haddock to basic macaroni cheese lifts this dish to another level entirely.

Serves 2 | **Takes 20** minutes to prepare, **20** minutes to cook | **13½ POINTS** values per recipe | **438** calories per serving

225 ml (8 fl oz) skimmed milk
1½ tablespoons cornflour
200 g (7 oz) smoked haddock
100 g (3½ oz) dried macaroni
40 g (1½ oz) low fat mature cheese, grated
1 tablespoon freshly grated Parmesan cheese
1 spring onion, sliced
½ teaspoon Dijon mustard (optional)
50 g (1¾ oz) frozen peas
1 tomato, sliced

Method

1 Preheat the oven to Gas Mark 6/200°C/fan oven 180°C. Blend 2 tablespoons of milk with the cornflour in a small bowl. Set aside. Pour the rest of the milk over the haddock in a large, lidded pan. Cover and poach for 5 minutes. Remove the fish to a plate. Flake roughly. Reserve the poaching liquid.

2 Meanwhile, bring a pan of water to the boil and cook the macaroni according to the packet instructions. Drain and rinse in cold water.

3 Add the cornflour mixture to the poaching liquid and bring to the boil, stirring until thickened.

4 Mix the two cheeses together and then measure out 15 g (½ oz) for the topping and mix with the spring onion. Stir the rest of the cheese into the sauce, plus the mustard, if using. Mix in the frozen peas, the smoked haddock and the macaroni and transfer to an ovenproof dish.

5 Top with the sliced tomato and scatter with the cheese and spring onion mixture. Bake in the oven for 20 minutes or until bubbling and golden brown.

6 1/2
POINTS
VALUE

Sausage and potato hotpot

This warming and hearty dish is perfect on a chilly evening. Serve with lightly cooked green cabbage, for no additional *POINTS* values.

Serves 4 | **Takes 20** minutes to prepare, **1** hour to cook | **18 *POINTS*** values per recipe | **390** calories per serving

low fat cooking spray
8 thick low fat sausages
*2 **onions**, cut into wedges*
*4 **carrots**, peeled and sliced*
2 tablespoons plain flour
150 ml (5 fl oz) medium cider
300 ml (10 fl oz) hot chicken stock
*1 tablespoon chopped fresh **thyme***
*600 g (1 lb 5 oz) **potatoes**, peeled and sliced thinly*
freshly ground black pepper

Method

1 Preheat the oven to Gas Mark 4/180°C/fan oven 160°C.

2 Heat a non stick frying pan until hot and spray with the cooking spray. Brown the sausages for 4 minutes, turning to colour evenly. Transfer to a 20 x 25 cm (8 x 10 inch) baking dish.

3 Add the onions and carrots to the frying pan and cook for 4–5 minutes until coloured. Mix in the flour, followed by the cider, stock and thyme. Bring to a simmer and then pour all over the sausages. Layer the sliced potatoes on top and spray with the cooking spray. Season with black pepper and cover the dish with foil.

4 Bake in the oven for 45 minutes until the potatoes are tender then remove the foil and cook for a further 15 minutes to brown the top.

Why not try... a vegetarian version with eight Quorn Cumberland sausages, and replace the chicken stock with vegetable stock, for 4 ***POINTS*** values per serving.

Smart ideas...

Don't store potatoes and onions next to each other – it will cause them to spoil more quickly. Keep bananas out of your fruit bowl too since they speed up the ripening process of other fruits.

4 1/2
POINTS
VALUE

chapter

Celebrate 8

Eating in is a great way to **enjoy the company of family and friends**. For a fabulous meal, why not begin with an easy but impressive starter such as Sweet Chilli Prawns with Mango Salad followed by the Tequila Chicken – or for fish lovers, there is Lemon Peppered Tuna with Courgettes. Many recipes can be **prepared ahead**, making it all much simpler on the day. That way, you can spend less time in the kitchen and more time with your friends.

Salmon fillet with roasted pepper salsa on page 142

Balsamic onion and goat's cheese tart

Serve this delicious and flaky pastry tart with a rocket salad, for no additional *POINTS* values.

Serves 6 | **Takes 20** minutes to prepare, **15** minutes to cook | **28½ *POINTS*** values per recipe | **206** calories per serving

low fat cooking spray
450 g (1 lb) onions, sliced thinly
4 teaspoons chopped fresh thyme
3 tablespoons balsamic vinegar
300 ml (10 fl oz) hot vegetable stock
200 g (7 oz) puff pastry
1 teaspoon plain flour, for rolling
1 tablespoon skimmed milk (optional)
100 g (3½ oz) individual rinded goat's cheese e.g. Somerset

Method

1 Heat a lidded, non stick frying pan until hot and spray with the cooking spray. Add the onions and cook for 2 minutes then add half the thyme, balsamic vinegar and stock. Cover the pan and cook for 10 minutes over a medium heat until softened.

2 Remove the lid, increase the heat and cook until all the stock has evaporated. Then carry on cooking, stirring frequently, until the onions are slightly caramelised, taking care that they don't catch and burn on the base of the pan. Preheat the oven to Gas Mark 6/200°C/fan oven 180°C.

3 Roll the pastry out on a floured surface to a rectangle measuring 25 x 33 cm (10 x 13 inches) then transfer to a non stick baking sheet. Mark a 2 cm (¾ inch) border around the edge and glaze the border with the milk, if using. Prick the pastry base with a fork then spread out the onions within the border.

4 Bake the tart for 10 minutes. Slice the goat's cheese into six half moons and arrange on the tart, evenly spaced. Bake for a further 5 minutes until just starting to melt. Sprinkle the rest of the thyme over the tart and cut into sixths to serve.

Why not try... this tart topped with 100 g (3½ oz) crumbled feta cheese instead of goat's cheese, for the same ***POINTS*** values per serving.

Cook's tip... If you want to prepare the tart ahead, cook the onions then cool them at the end of step two by spreading them out on a plate. Prepare the pastry base and chill until needed. When you're ready to cook the tart, top the base with the onions and finish it all off as directed in step 4.

4 1/2
POINTS
VALUE

Gougère with mushroom filling

A gougère is a savoury choux pastry case baked with a filling which, on this occasion, is a richly flavoured mushroom and olive mixture.

Serves 6 | **Takes 20** minutes to prepare, **40** minutes to cook | **22½ *POINTS*** values per recipe | **250** calories per serving

low fat cooking spray
100 g (3½ oz) plain flour
75 g (2¾ oz) low fat spread
3 **eggs**, *lightly beaten*
50 g (1¾ oz) Gruyère cheese, cut into 5 mm (¼ inch) dice, plus 15 g (½ oz) grated finely
salt and freshly ground black pepper

For the filling
750 g (1 lb 10 oz) open cup **mushrooms**, *chopped roughly*
3 **garlic cloves**, *crushed*
75 g (2¾ oz) pitted **black olives in brine**, *drained*
2 teaspoons **dried herbes de Provence** *or mixed* **dried herbs**
200 g (7 oz) **cherry tomatoes**, *halved*

Method

1 Preheat the oven to Gas Mark 6/200°C/fan oven 180°C. Spray a large, ovenproof baking dish with the cooking spray. Fold a piece of baking parchment or foil in half, then open out and sift on the flour and a pinch of salt. Add a grinding of black pepper.

2 Place the low fat spread in a non stick saucepan with 200 ml (7 fl oz) cold water and bring to a rolling boil. Remove from the heat and quickly tip in the flour. Stir briskly until the mixture comes together as a ball of dough. Sit the pan in a basin of cold water for about 10 minutes or until the dough is cool.

3 Gradually mix the beaten egg into the dough until you have a smooth and shiny batter that drops easily from the spoon. Stir in the diced cheese then dollop spoonfuls around the edge of the baking dish, just touching each other, leaving a hole in the centre for the filling. Bake for 25 minutes.

4 Meanwhile, for the filling, place the mushrooms, garlic and 2 tablespoons of water in a large, lidded saucepan. Cook, covered, for 5 minutes until the mushrooms release their juices. Remove the lid and continue cooking until the juices have evaporated.

5 Stir the olives and herbs in with the mushrooms and cook, uncovered, for 10 minutes. Spoon the filling into the centre of the gougère, scatter the tomatoes over the top and and sprinkle the grated cheese over the risen pastry case. Bake for 15 minutes and then serve immediately.

Cook's tip... Instead of using fresh cherry tomatoes, you might prefer to use a 400 g can of chopped tomatoes. Add it with the olives and herbs in step 5 and omit scattering over the fresh tomatoes.

4
POINTS
VALUE

Tequila chicken

A vibrantly coloured dish that looks wonderful on the plate.

Serves 6 | **Takes 20** minutes to prepare + marinating, **20** minutes to cook | **18½ *POINTS*** values per recipe | **203** calories per serving

3 tablespoons tequila
4 rounded teaspoons clear honey
finely grated zest and juice of a lime
6 x 125 g (4½ oz) **skinless boneless chicken breasts**
freshly ground black pepper

For the salsa
2 x 125 g (4½ oz) **corn on the cob**
low fat cooking spray
1 red **pepper***, de-seeded and diced*
3 heaped tablespoons chopped fresh **coriander**
1 small red **onion***, chopped finely*
1 lime

Method

1 Stir the tequila, honey, lime zest and juice together in a small bowl. Season with black pepper and pour into a large plastic food bag. Slash each chicken breast a few times and add to the marinade, turning to coat. Seal the bag and marinate in the fridge for at least 30 minutes. Preheat the oven to Gas Mark 6/200°C/fan oven 180°C.

2 Meanwhile, for the salsa, preheat the grill to medium high and spray the corn on the cob with the cooking spray. Grill for 15 minutes, turning to colour evenly. Leave to cool then slice the toasted corn kernels away from the cob. Mix the corn with the pepper, coriander and red onion. Finely grate the zest from half the lime and add to the salsa, along with the squeezed juice of the whole lime.

3 Remove the chicken from its marinade and place on a non stick baking tray. Cook in the oven for 20 minutes or until cooked, glazing with some of the marinade halfway through. Serve with the salsa spooned over the chicken.

Cook's tip... If you don't have any tequila, you can use vodka or whisky in the marinade instead, for the same ***POINTS*** values.

Smart ideas...

Make your Weight Watchers recipes for friends and family – you'll get lots of compliments and they'll be amazed that you can lose weight with such tasty dishes.

3
POINTS
VALUE

Thai cod filo parcels

5 *POINTS* VALUE

Serve with 60 g (2 oz) dried rice per person, cooked according to packet instructions, for an extra 3 *POINTS* values per serving.

Serves 4 | **Takes 15** minutes to prepare, **15** minutes to cook | **20 *POINTS*** values per recipe | **354** calories per serving

1 teaspoon Thai red curry paste
75 g (2¾ oz) **low fat soft cheese**
4 heaped tablespoons chopped fresh **coriander**
3 **spring onions***, chopped finely*
finely grated zest and juice of ½ a lime
4 x 45 g (1½ oz) large sheets frozen filo pastry, defrosted
low fat cooking spray
4 x 110 g (4 oz) pieces skinless **cod fillet**
4 tablespoons reduced fat mayonnaise
50 g (1¾ oz) **very low fat natural fromage frais**

Method

1 Preheat the oven to Gas Mark 6/200°C/fan oven 180°C. In a small bowl, mix the curry paste with the low fat soft cheese, half the coriander, the spring onions and half of the lime zest.

2 Spray the filo with cooking spray and fold each sheet in half to make a square. Put a piece of cod in the centre and spread with a quarter of the paste. Wrap neatly in the filo then place on a non stick baking tray, sprayed with the cooking spray.

3 Bake in the oven for 15 minutes until crisp and golden brown. Meanwhile, mix the rest of the lime zest and juice with the mayonnaise, fromage frais and the remaining coriander. Serve with the hot parcels.

Why not try... making these parcels with four 110 g (4 oz) pieces of skinless salmon fillet, for 7 ***POINTS*** values per person.

Lemon peppered tuna with courgettes

2 *POINTS* VALUE

A simple but stunning recipe for when you want to treat someone special. Serve with 150 g (5½ oz) new potatoes per person, for an additional 1½ *POINTS* values per serving.

Serves 2 | **Takes 20** minutes | **4½ *POINTS*** values per recipe | **159** calories per serving

low fat cooking spray
2 **courgettes***, cut into 3 mm (⅛ inch) slices lengthways*
½ a lemon
½ red **chilli***, de-seeded and diced*
½ teaspoon crushed peppercorns
2 x 100 g (3½ oz) **tuna steaks**

Method

1 Preheat a griddle pan or the grill to a medium high heat. Spray the courgette slices with the cooking spray and cook or grill for about 2 minutes on each side until browned and tender. Transfer to a plate and keep warm.

2 Meanwhile, finely grate the zest from the lemon and then cut the lemon half into two wedges. Mix the zest with the chilli and crushed peppercorns. Spray the tuna steaks with the cooking spray and coat with the lemon pepper mixture, pressing on well.

3 Cook or grill the tuna steaks and lemon wedges for 2–3 minutes on each side, depending on the thickness of the tuna, until the fish is just cooked through. Serve with the courgette ribbons, with the cooked lemon wedges to squeeze over.

2
POINTS
VALUE

Peppered beef steak with mushroom sauce

A serving of Celeriac and Mustard Mash (on page 160) and some sugar snap peas is delicious with these steaks, for an additional 2 ***POINTS*** values per person.

Serves 4 | **Takes 30** minutes | **14½ *POINTS*** values per recipe | **215** calories per serving

4 x 110 g (4 oz) **fillet steaks**
1 teaspoon peppercorns
1 teaspoon coriander seeds

For the sauce
low fat cooking spray
350 g (12 oz) **mushrooms**, *chopped roughly*
2 **garlic cloves**
200 ml (7 fl oz) hot beef stock
60 g (2 oz) **low fat soft cheese**
1 tablespoon cornflour
1 teaspoon lemon juice
2 tablespoons snipped fresh chives

Method

1 Remove the steaks from the fridge 30 minutes before cooking. Crush the peppercorns and coriander seeds together with a pestle and mortar and press on to both sides of the steaks. Set aside.

2 Heat a large, lidded saucepan until hot and spray with the cooking spray. Add the mushrooms and cook for 1 minute then add the garlic and 2 tablespoons of the stock. Cover and cook for 5 minutes. Stir in the soft cheese, followed by the remaining stock, and bring to a simmer.

3 Blend the cornflour with a little cold water then add to the mushroom sauce and stir until thickened. Add lemon to taste, stir in the chives and keep warm.

4 To cook the steaks, heat a non stick frying pan until hot and spray with the cooking spray. Fry the steaks for 1½ minutes on each side over a high heat to brown, then reduce the heat to medium. Cook for a further 3 minutes on each side for medium rare and 5 minutes on each side for well done. Rest the steaks for a couple of minutes before serving with the mushroom sauce spooned over.

Cook's tip... The sauce can be made ahead of time and then reheated for spooning over in step 4.

Smart ideas...

Low fat soft cheese is very versatile – use it to add richness to sauces, toss it through pasta or simply enjoy it as a spread.

3 1/2
POINTS
VALUE

Sweet chilli prawns with mango salad

2½ *POINTS* VALUE

This is an easy but impressive starter for a supper with friends.

Serves 4 | **Takes 15** minutes | **10½** ***POINTS*** values per recipe | **149** calories per serving

20 shelled raw tiger **prawns**
3 tablespoons Thai sweet chilli sauce
juice of ½ a lime
100 g (3½ oz) **mixed leaf salad with rocket**
1 **mango**, *peeled and sliced thinly*
1 **avocado**, *peeled, stoned and sliced thinly*

Method

1 Preheat the grill to medium high. Thread five prawns on to each of four metal skewers and arrange on a non stick baking tray. Mix the chilli sauce and lime juice together and drizzle over the prawns. Grill for 2 minutes on each side or until the prawns are cooked through.

2 Meanwhile, divide the salad leaves between four plates and top with the mango and avocado. Place a skewer of prawns on top of each salad and drizzle with the juices from the baking tray. Serve straightaway.

Cook's tip... The mango can be peeled before slicing, using a swivel-bladed vegetable peeler. When preparing the avocado however, it is easier to slice the avocado in half first and remove the stone. Then run a spoon between the peel and the flesh of the avocado to lift each half out in one piece and slice.

Almond glazed duck with asparagus

4½ *POINTS* VALUE

A lovely recipe for a special dinner for two. Serve with a 150 g (5½ oz) portion of cooked wild or Jasmine rice, for an extra 3 ***POINTS*** values per serving.

Serves 2 | **Takes 20** minutes | **9** ***POINTS*** values per recipe | **308** calories per serving

300 g (10½ oz) **asparagus spears**, *trimmed*
low fat cooking spray
2 x 125 g (4½ oz) **skinless duck breast fillets**
2 tablespoons soy sauce
4 rounded teaspoons clear honey
15 g (½ oz) flaked almonds
½ red **chilli**, *de-seeded and diced*

Method

1 Preheat the oven to Gas Mark 6/200°C/fan oven 180°C. Place the asparagus in a shallow roasting tin, spray with the cooking spray and drizzle with 2 tablespoons water. Roast in the oven for 8 minutes.

2 Meanwhile, heat a non stick frying pan until hot and spray with the cooking spray. Brown the duck for 2 minutes on each side over a high heat for duck that will still be slightly pink in the centre, or cook for 3 minutes on each side if you prefer it more cooked through.

3 Remove the pan from the hob and add the soy sauce, honey, almonds and chilli. Turn the duck to coat in the sauce.

4 Stir the asparagus and make room for the duck. Nestle the duck breasts among the asparagus and spoon the sauce all over. Roast in the oven for 8 minutes and serve on warmed plates.

Why not try... making this recipe with two 125 g (4½ oz) skinless chicken breast fillets, for 4 ***POINTS*** values per person. Brown the chicken for 5 minutes on each side in step 2.

4 1/2
POINTS
VALUE

Salmon fillet with roasted pepper salsa

This meal has a wonderfully vibrant combination of colours, flavours and textures.

Serves 4 | **Takes 20** minutes to prepare, **20–25** minutes to cook | **16 *POINTS*** values per recipe | **296** calories per serving

2 yellow **peppers**
150 g (5½ oz) **cherry tomatoes**, *quartered*
1 **spring onion**, *chopped finely*
2 teaspoons lemon juice
low fat cooking spray
2 **garlic cloves**, *sliced*
450 g (1 lb) young leaf **spinach**
4 x 125 g (4½ oz) skinned **salmon fillets**

Method

1 Preheat the oven to Gas Mark 6/200°C/fan oven 180°C. Place the peppers on a non stick baking tray and roast for 20–25 minutes until the skins are beginning to brown and blister. Place in a bowl, cover with clingfilm and leave to cool. When cool enough to handle, peel off the skins, de-seed and then cut the peppers into thin strips. Mix with the cherry tomatoes, spring onion and lemon juice to make the salsa. Set aside.

2 Heat a large saucepan until hot and spray with the cooking spray. Fry the garlic and cook, stirring until golden then pile in the spinach a bit at a time, stirring until it has wilted.

3 Heat a non stick frying pan until hot and spray with the cooking spray. Add the salmon and cook for 3 minutes on each side over a high heat.

4 Serve the salmon on a bed of garlic spinach with the salsa spooned over the top.

Cook's tip... The salmon fillets can also be baked in the oven, loosely covered with foil, for 12–15 minutes at Gas Mark 4/180°C/fan oven 160°C.

Citrus pork steaks with potato salad

A smart dish for a kitchen supper with friends.

Serves 4 | **Takes 25** minutes | **20½ *POINTS*** values per recipe | **385** calories per serving

700 g (1 lb 9 oz) small **new potatoes**, *halved*
250 g (9 oz) **fine green beans**, *halved*
1½ teaspoons peppercorns, crushed
finely grated zest and juice of an orange
4 x 125 g (4½ oz) **lean pork loin steaks**, *trimmed of all fat*
low fat cooking spray
juice of ½ a lemon
2 rounded teaspoons honey
3 tablespoons low fat French dressing

Method

1 Bring a large saucepan of water to the boil, add the potatoes and cook for 12– 15 minutes or until almost tender. Add the green beans and cook for a further 5 minutes. Drain thoroughly.

2 Meanwhile, mix the crushed peppercorns with the orange zest and press on to the pork steaks. Heat a non stick frying pan until hot and spray with the cooking spray. Fry the pork steaks for 5 minutes on each side, then add the orange juice, lemon juice, honey and 2 tablespoons of water. Bubble gently for 2 minutes.

3 Toss the potatoes and beans with the French dressing. Serve the pork steaks on a bed of the warm potato and bean salad, with the pan juices drizzled on top.

5
POINTS
VALUE

Chicken, Stilton and cranberry strudels

6 POINTS VALUE

A superbly flavoursome recipe using just a handful of ingredients, these strudels are very easy to prepare and can be kept in the fridge until ready to bake.

Serves 6 | **Takes 10** minutes to prepare, **20** minutes to cook | **36½ *POINTS*** values per recipe | **310** calories per serving

6 x 45 g (1½ oz) sheets frozen filo pastry, defrosted
low fat cooking spray
6 tablespoons cranberry sauce
6 x 125 g (4½ oz) **skinless boneless chicken breasts**
75 g (2¾ oz) Stilton cheese, crumbled
freshly ground black pepper

Method

1 Preheat the oven to Gas Mark 6/200°C/fan oven 180°C.

2 Unroll the filo, but keep the sheets in a stack so that they don't dry out. For each strudel, spray a sheet of filo with the cooking spray and fold in half to give a square. Spray again with the cooking spray then place 1 tablespoon of cranberry sauce near the centre of the top edge.

3 Sit a chicken breast on top, season with black pepper and press one sixth of the Stilton on to the chicken. Fold in the sides of the pastry, then roll up to enclose completely. Repeat to make a total of six strudels.

4 Place the strudels on a non stick baking tray sprayed with the cooking spray and bake for 20 minutes until golden brown and crisp.

Lamb steaks with roasted vegetables

A peppery watercress, spinach and rocket salad goes well with this, for no extra *POINTS* values.

Serves 4 | **Takes 15** minutes to prepare, **35** minutes to cook | **17 *POINTS*** values per recipe | **279** calories per serving

750 g (1 lb 10 oz), **butternut squash**, *peeled, de-seeded and cut in half horizontally*
600 g (1 lb 5 oz) **potatoes**, *unpeeled and cut into wedges*
low fat cooking spray
2 teaspoons cumin seeds
450 g (1 lb) **lean lamb leg steaks**, *trimmed of all fat*
1 red **onion**, *sliced*
2 **garlic cloves**, *crushed*
250 g (9 oz) **cherry tomatoes** *on the vine, snipped into clusters*
freshly ground black pepper

Method

1 Preheat the oven to Gas Mark 6/200°C/fan oven 180°C. Cut each of the butternut squash halves into eight wedges. Arrange the squash and potato wedges in a large roasting tin in a single layer, spray with the cooking spray and scatter with the cumin seeds. Roast in the oven for 25 minutes.

2 Heat a non stick frying pan until hot and spray with the cooking spray. Season the lamb with black pepper and cook for 1½ minutes on each side over a high heat to brown.

3 Scatter the red onion and garlic in among the roasted wedges in the tray and nestle the lamb steaks and cherry tomatoes on top. Roast for 10 minutes then serve.

4
POINTS
VALUE

Honey mustard Quorn fillets with baby vegetables

Pretty as a picture with its medley of baby vegetables, this is a most attractive vegetarian main course.

Serves 4 | **Takes 25** minutes | **12½ *POINTS*** values per recipe | **234** calories per serving

400 g (14 oz) small **new potatoes***, halved*
150 g (5½ oz) **Chantenay carrots***, scrubbed and trimmed*
150 g (5½ oz) **baby corn***, halved*
100 g (3½ oz) **sugar snap peas**
low fat cooking spray
8 frozen **Quorn Deli Chicken Style Fillets**
juice of a lemon
2 tablespoons coarse grain mustard
4 rounded teaspoons clear honey

Method

1 Bring a large, lidded saucepan of water to the boil, add the new potatoes, cover and cook for 10 minutes. Add the carrots, cover and cook for 5 minutes then finally add the baby corn and sugar snaps. Cover and cook for 4 minutes more, then drain the vegetables.

2 Meanwhile, heat a large, lidded, non stick frying pan until hot and spray with the cooking spray. Brown the Quorn fillets for 5–6 minutes over a high heat, turning to colour evenly. Reduce the heat and add the lemon juice, mustard and honey plus 2 tablespoons of water. Cover the pan and simmer gently for 8 minutes.

3 Push the Quorn fillets to the side of the pan then add the drained vegetables and toss through the sauce. Serve the Quorn on a bed of the glazed vegetables.

Why not try... this recipe with four 125 g (4½ oz) skinless chicken breast fillets instead of the Quorn fillets. Brown the chicken for 8–10 minutes before adding the sauce in step 2, for 3½ ***POINTS*** values per serving. 7

Smart ideas...

Try to make dinner an occasion as often as possible – it's good to appreciate your food at leisure, accompanied by lots of good conversation.

3
POINTS
VALUE

chapter

9 Something on the side

Look no further for a great selection of **inspiring and filling** side dishes to **transform everyday meals** into something special. Recipes such as Oven Sautéed Spiced Potatoes or Broccoli with Cheese and Tomatoes are just the thing to make a simple meal sensational. And with a Wensleydale and Spring Onion Scone, a Cornbread Muffin or some Rosemary and Olive Soda Bread on the side, a warming bowl of soup is just sublime.

Roasted new potatoes with shallots on page 154

Potato, carrot and leek bake

Here's a good dish to serve with a simple roast chicken, especially as you can just pop it in the oven to cook with very little fuss.

Serves 6 | **Takes 20** minutes to prepare, **1¼** hours to cook | **11 *POINTS*** values per recipe | **159** calories per serving

low fat cooking spray
2 leeks, trimmed and sliced
1 tablespoon chopped fresh thyme
500 ml (18 fl oz) hot vegetable stock
900 g (2 lb) floury potatoes such as Maris Piper or Rooster, peeled and sliced thinly
250 g (9 oz) carrots, peeled and sliced thinly
300 ml (10 fl oz) skimmed milk
salt and freshly ground black pepper

Method

1 Preheat the oven to Gas Mark 4/180°C/fan oven 160°C. Heat a lidded, non stick saucepan until hot and spray with the cooking spray. Stir in the leeks and thyme then add 3 tablespoons of the stock and cook, covered, for 3–4 minutes until tender.

2 Spray a large ovenproof dish, measuring about 20 x 30 cm (8 x 12 inches) and 5 cm (2 inches) deep, with the cooking spray then layer in half the potatoes. Top with the carrots and the cooked leeks, seasoning as you go, and then cover with the remaining potatoes. Pour in the stock and milk to just cover the vegetables. Cover the dish with a sheet of foil, place on a baking tray and cook in the oven for 1 hour until tender.

3 Remove the foil, spray the top layer of potatoes with the cooking spray and return to the oven for 15 minutes until browned. When you scoop out the bake, you'll find a sauce at the bottom which should be spooned over the vegetables to serve.

Cook's tip... You can cut down on the preparation time for this recipe if you've got a food processor or a hand-held mandolin to slice the potatoes and carrots.

Smart ideas...

Plan the menus for the week before you go shopping. You'll be inspired to try new recipes or new ingredients, rather than just buying the same few familiar foods every week. It will also help you to keep to your shopping list, saving you money.

2 POINTS VALUE

French style cabbage

½ POINTS VALUE

This recipe for cabbage is a wonderful way to liven up an economical vegetable.

Serves 4 | **Takes 10** minutes | **3 *POINTS*** values per recipe | **55** calories per serving

1 green cabbage, around 500 g (1 lb 2 oz), shredded
60 g (2 oz) half fat crème fraîche
freshly grated nutmeg
a squeeze of lemon juice
freshly ground black pepper

Method

1 Place the cabbage in a large, lidded saucepan and add boiling water to come halfway up the cabbage. Cover the pan and cook rapidly for 4–5 minutes until the cabbage is tender.

2 Drain well in a colander.

3 In the same pan, gently warm the crème fraîche, adding plenty of nutmeg and black pepper. Toss the cabbage in the creamy sauce, adding lemon juice to taste. Serve immediately.

Oven sautéed spiced potatoes

Crisp, diced potatoes make an appetising accompaniment to simple grilled fish or meat.

Serves 4 | **Takes 15** minutes to prepare, **30** minutes to cook | **10 *POINTS*** values per recipe | **196** calories per serving

900 g (2 lb) potatoes, peeled and cut into 2 cm (¾ inch) dice
½ vegetable stock cube, crumbled
low fat cooking spray
1 teaspoon smoked paprika
1 teaspoon cumin seeds
1 red onion, chopped roughly

Method

1 Preheat the oven to Gas Mark 6/200°C/fan oven 180°C. Place a large roasting tray in the oven to preheat.

2 Bring a large saucepan of water to the boil, add the potatoes and the stock cube and cook for 6 minutes until just tender and starting to soften at the edges. Drain then shake lightly to roughen the edges. Spray the potatoes with the cooking spray and mix with the smoked paprika and cumin seeds.

3 Spread out the spiced potatoes on the hot roasting tray in a single layer then roast in the oven for 20 minutes.

4 Scatter the red onion in among the potatoes. Spray again with the cooking spray and cook for a further 10 minutes. Serve immediately.

Why not try... changing the spices in this recipe to suit your mood and experimenting with what's in your spice rack. For example, you might like to use 1 tablespoon of medium curry powder or 1 tablespoon of Cajun spice instead of the smoked paprika and cumin seeds.

2 1/2
POINTS
VALUE

Roasted new potatoes with shallots

Don't be alarmed by the fact that a whole garlic bulb is used – when the cloves are baked in their skins, the flavour becomes sweet and very mellow.

Serves 4 | **Takes 10** minutes to prepare, **35** minutes to cook | **8 *POINTS*** values per recipe | **181** calories per serving

750 g (1 lb 10 oz) **new potatoes**, *halved*
low fat cooking spray
1 **garlic bulb**, *cloves separated*
250 g (9 oz) **shallots**, *peeled and halved*
1 red **pepper**, *de-seeded and chopped roughly*
1 yellow **pepper**, *de-seeded and chopped roughly*

Method

1 Preheat the oven to Gas Mark 7/220°C/fan oven 200°C. Place a large roasting tin in the oven to preheat.

2 Bring a large saucepan of water to the boil, add the potatoes and cook for 7 minutes. Drain and spray with the cooking spray, toss and then spread out in the hot roasting tin. Roast in the oven for 15 minutes.

3 Meanwhile, toss the garlic cloves, shallots and peppers together and spray with the cooking spray. Mix in with the potatoes and stir well. Roast for a further 20 minutes, stirring halfway through. To serve, cut the ends off the cooked garlic cloves and squeeze out the soft garlic to mix with the roasted vegetables on your plate.

Cook's tip... To make it easier to peel shallots, place them in a bowl and cover with boiling water for a couple of minutes to loosen the skins.

Jewelled couscous

Add some pizzaz to a plate of plain grilled meat or fish with this colourful side dish.

Serves 4 | **Takes 15** minutes | **14½ *POINTS*** values per recipe | **251** calories per serving

low fat cooking spray
1 bunch **spring onions**, *sliced*
200 g (7 oz) frozen **peas**
75 g (2¾ oz) ready to eat dried apricots, chopped finely
200 g (7 oz) dried **couscous**
juice of ½ a lemon
400 ml (14 fl oz) hot vegetable stock

Method

1 Heat a lidded saucepan until hot and spray with the cooking spray. Stir fry the spring onions for 1 minute, add the peas and cook for 1 minute more.

2 Add the apricots, couscous and lemon juice to the pan and pour in the hot stock. Bring to the boil, stir and then cover the pan. Remove from the heat and leave to stand and soften for 8 minutes.

3 Fluff up the couscous with a fork before serving.

Why not try... using this recipe as the basis for a salad. Stir in 150 g (5½ oz) diced cherry tomatoes. Then top with either 100 g (3½ oz) sliced cooked chicken breast per person, for 6 ***POINTS*** values per serving or 40 g (1½ oz) crumbled feta cheese per person, for 7 ***POINTS*** values per serving.

3 1/2
POINTS
VALUE

Spiced brown rice and mushroom pilau

2½ POINTS VALUE

Enjoy this spiced rice with a tasty curry.

Serves 4 | **Takes 10** minutes to prepare, **35** minutes to cook + resting | **10** ***POINTS*** values per recipe | **204** calories per serving

low fat cooking spray
1 **onion**, *sliced thinly*
1 teaspoon black onion seeds
1 teaspoon cumin seeds
1 piece cinnamon stick
¼ teaspoon ground turmeric
2 **bay leaves**
200 g (7 oz) chestnut **mushrooms**, *sliced*
200 g (7 oz) **brown basmati rice**
500 ml (18 fl oz) boiling water

Method

1 Heat a large, lidded saucepan until hot and spray with the cooking spray. Cook the onion for 4 minutes over a high heat until browned, stirring once or twice, adding a splash of water if it starts to stick. Add all the spices and the bay leaves and cook for 1 minute, stirring, then mix in the mushrooms plus 2 tablespoons of water. Cover and cook for 2 minutes.

2 Stir the rice into the pan with the mushroom mixture and add the boiling water. Bring to the boil, give the rice a final stir then cover tightly with a lid and reduce the heat to a very low setting. Cook undisturbed for 35 minutes by which time all the liquid should be absorbed and the rice will be tender.

3 Remove from the heat, take off the lid and cover the rice with a clean tea towel. Leave to stand for 5 minutes, while the rice fluffs up.

Cauliflower and broccoli gratin

1 POINTS VALUE

This makes a delicious accompaniment to the Roast Beef with Onion Yorkshire Pudding (on page 96).

Serves 4 | **Takes 20** minutes | **4½** ***POINTS*** values per recipe | **110** calories per serving

300 g (10½ oz) **cauliflower** *florets*
175 g (6 oz) **broccoli** *florets*
2 tablespoons cornflour
150 ml (5 fl oz) **skimmed milk**
150 ml (5 fl oz) hot vegetable stock
60 g (2 oz) **low fat soft cheese**
15 g (½ oz) freshly grated Parmesan cheese
freshly ground black pepper

Method

1 Preheat the grill to medium hot. Bring a large pan of water to the boil. Add the cauliflower and cook for 3 minutes then add the broccoli. Cook for 3 minutes more. Drain well in a colander then transfer to an ovenproof baking dish.

2 Meanwhile, place the cornflour in a non stick saucepan and gradually blend in the milk to make a smooth paste, followed by the stock. Bring to the boil, stirring until thickened. Simmer for 2 minutes then mix in the soft cheese and a seasoning of black pepper.

3 Pour the sauce over the cauliflower and broccoli, top with the cheese and grill for 4–5 minutes until browned and bubbling.

1 POINTS VALUE

Wensleydale and spring onion scones

1½ POINTS VALUE

Delicious when fresh and still slightly warm.

Makes 12 | **Takes 15** minutes to prepare, **12** minutes to cook | **20 *POINTS*** values per recipe | **97** calories per scone

225 g (8 oz) self raising flour
½ teaspoon baking powder
½ teaspoon dried mustard
40 g (1½ oz) low fat spread
50 g (1¾ oz) Wensleydale cheese, grated
*2 **spring onions**, chopped*
*150 ml (5 fl oz) **skimmed milk** plus 1 tablespoon to glaze*
low fat cooking spray
salt and freshly ground black pepper

Method

1 Preheat the oven to Gas Mark 7/220°C/fan oven 200°C. Reserve 1 tablespoon of the flour for rolling out. Sift the rest of the flour, the baking powder and mustard into a mixing bowl and add some seasoning. Rub in the low fat spread until the mixture looks like breadcrumbs then stir in the Wensleydale cheese and the spring onions.

2 Add enough of the milk to bring the dough together as a clean ball. Dust the work surface with the reserved flour and pat or roll the dough out to a thickness of 2 cm (¾ inch). Cut out twelve 5 cm (2 inches) rounds using a cutter, re-rolling the dough as necessary.

3 Place on a baking tray sprayed with the cooking spray and brush the tops with milk. Bake for 10–12 minutes until risen, golden brown and firm. Remove the scones from the oven and cool only slightly.

Why not try... adding 30 g (1¼ oz) chopped wafer thin ham to the scone mixture. The ***POINTS*** values will remain the same.

Broccoli with cheese and tomatoes

½ POINTS VALUE

Broccoli is one of the top-selling green vegetables in the UK, so here's a new way with an old favourite that's very easy to prepare.

Serves 2 | **Takes 10** minutes | **1 *POINTS*** value per recipe | **54** calories per serving

*150 g (5½ oz) small florets of **broccoli***
low fat cooking spray
*2 **tomatoes**, chopped roughly*
*1 tablespoon shredded fresh **basil***
2 teaspoons freshly grated Parmesan cheese
freshly ground black pepper

Method

1 Preheat the grill to medium hot. Bring a pan of water to the boil, add the broccoli and cook for 3 minutes until just tender. Drain well.

2 Meanwhile, heat a small, non stick saucepan until hot. Spray with cooking spray and cook the tomatoes for about 3 minutes until softened. Add the basil and a seasoning of black pepper. Mix with the broccoli and transfer to an ovenproof dish.

3 Scatter the cheese on top and grill for 2 minutes. Serve immediately.

1/2
POINTS
VALUE

Celeriac and mustard mash

2 *POINTS* VALUE

Celeriac may not be the most attractive of vegetables with its gnarled, knobbly appearance, but don't be put off by how it looks. It has a delicate flavour, similar to celery, that combines well with potato in this creamy mash.

Serves 4 | **Takes 10** minutes to prepare, **20** minutes to cook | **8½ *POINTS*** values per recipe | **212** calories per serving

*1 **celeriac**, approx 600 g (1 lb 5 oz), peeled and cut into even sized pieces*
*600 g (1 lb 5 oz) **potatoes**, peeled and cut into even sized pieces*
*100 ml (3½ fl oz) **skimmed milk***
*60 g (2 oz) **low fat soft cheese***
1 tablespoon coarse grain mustard

Method

1 Bring a large lidded saucepan of water to the boil and add the celeriac and potatoes. Cover and cook gently for 15–20 minutes until tender. Drain in a colander and leave to steam dry for a couple of minutes.
2 Meanwhile, heat the milk in the saucepan. Return the potatoes and celeriac to the pan and mash into the milk, adding the soft cheese and mustard.

Cook's tip... The easiest way to peel the celeriac is to carefully cut away the skin with a kitchen knife.

Cornbread muffins

These golden savoury muffins are perfect with a bowl of zero *POINTS* value soup such as the Mediterranean Vegetable Soup (on page 24).

Makes 12 | **Takes 10** minutes to prepare, **15–20** minutes to cook | **20½ *POINTS*** values per recipe | **118** calories per muffin

low fat cooking spray
150 g (5½ oz) self raising flour
2 teaspoons baking powder
½ teaspoon salt
125 g (4½ oz) dried polenta
*½ red **pepper**, de-seeded and diced*
*1 **egg**, beaten*
60 g (2 oz) low fat spread, melted
*300 ml (10 fl oz) **skimmed milk***
freshly ground black pepper

Method

1 Preheat the oven to Gas Mark 6/200°C/fan oven 180°C. Spray a non stick 12 hole muffin tin with the cooking spray.
2 Sift the flour, baking powder and salt into a mixing bowl. Stir in the polenta, red pepper and some black pepper.
3 In a separate bowl, mix together the egg, melted low fat spread and milk. Pour into the dry ingredients and stir until just combined. The batter will be quite wet and sloppy – this is how it should be to ensure the muffins are moist.
4 Divide between the holes of the muffin tin and bake for 15–20 minutes, or until a skewer inserted in the centre of a muffin comes out clean.
5 Cool in the tin for 5 minutes before turning out on to a wire rack to continue cooling.

1 1/2
POINTS
VALUE

3

2 POINTS VALUE

Rosemary and olive soda bread

Soda bread is very quick to make and is best eaten on the day it is made. However, any leftovers can easily be frozen.

Serves 6 | **Takes 10** minutes to prepare, **20–25** minutes to cook | **11½ *POINTS*** values per recipe | **129** calories per serving

200 g (7 oz) self raising flour
a pinch of salt
½ teaspoon bicarbonate of soda
30 g (1¼ oz) pitted black **olives in brine***, chopped*
2 teaspoons chopped fresh **rosemary** *plus a few small sprigs*
100 g (3½ oz) **low fat natural yogurt***, beaten with 3 tablespoons of water*
low fat cooking spray

Method

1 Preheat the oven to Gas Mark 7/220°C/fan oven 200°C. Sift the flour, salt and bicarbonate of soda into a mixing bowl and stir in the olives and chopped rosemary.

2 Add the yogurt mixture, stirring with a table knife to bring the dough together as a clean ball. Add a little extra water if needed.

3 Spray a baking tray with the cooking spray then press the bread dough out to a 15 cm (6 inches) disc on the tray. Mark into six wedges with a knife, but don't cut all the way through. Press the rosemary sprigs into the loaf.

4 Bake for 20–25 minutes or until the bread sounds hollow when the underside is tapped. Cool on a wire rack before cutting it into wedges.

Smart ideas...

Before you start cooking, take a couple of minutes to read a recipe through to make sure you're aware of the time needed for different stages. Then collect together all the ingredients and equipment before you begin.

2
POINTS
VALUE

chapter 10

Desserts and bakes

We all love to enjoy a treat and these wonderful recipes are ideal for the **occasional indulgence**. Many are so quick that you can easily whip something up if friends pop round unexpectedly. Surprise the family with an amazing Hot Chocolate Pudding or a lovely Rhubarb and Apple Sponge Pudding and **delight your guests every time** with the Lemon and Grape Cheesecake.

Lemon and grape cheesecake on page 166

Lemon and grape cheesecake

3 POINTS VALUE

4

This light and zingy-flavoured cheesecake is a great dessert to make ahead for a party.

Serves 8 | **Takes 20** minutes + **2** hours chilling | **25½ *POINTS*** values per recipe | **178** calories per serving

11.5 g sachet **lemon and lime sugar free jelly**
150 ml (5 fl oz) boiling water
finely grated zest and juice of a lemon
150 g (5½ oz) low fat digestive biscuits, crushed
60 g (2 oz) low fat spread, melted
200 g (7 oz) **low fat natural yogurt**
200 g (7 oz) **low fat soft cheese**
200 g (7 oz) red and green seedless **grapes**, *halved*

Method

1 Dissolve the jelly in the boiling water and add the lemon zest and juice. Leave to cool to room temperature (you can speed this up by standing the jug in a large bowl of cold water).

2 Mix the biscuit crumbs and low fat spread together and press firmly into a 20 cm (8 inch) loose bottom cake tin. Chill in the freezer for 10 minutes.

3 In a large bowl, whisk the yogurt and soft cheese together until smooth and then stir in the cooled jelly mixture. Pour over the biscuit base, cover and chill in the fridge for 2 hours or until set.

4 Remove the cheesecake from the tin and top with the halved grapes to serve.

Apricot and pistachio fool

This fruity fool is deliciously creamy and refreshing – and it's ready in minutes.

Serves 2 | **Takes 8** minutes | **5 *POINTS*** values per recipe | **203** calories per serving

411 g can **apricot halves in natural juice**, *drained*
150 g (5½ oz) pot low fat custard, chilled
150 g (5½ oz) **0% fat Greek yogurt**
15 g (½ oz) unsalted shelled pistachios, chopped finely

Method

1 Cut four of the apricot halves into thin slices and set aside.

2 Purée the remaining apricots in a liquidiser or with a hand held blender, then whizz in the custard and yogurt.

3 Divide between two dessert dishes, top with the sliced apricots and scatter with the pistachios. Chill before serving, if you wish.

Why not try... this fool with canned peaches in natural juice instead of apricots, for the same ***POINTS*** values. Add the finely grated zest of half a lime with the peaches.

2 1/2
POINTS
VALUE

Strawberry castles with fruity salsa

A lovely, fresh tasting, summery dessert.

Serves 4 | **Takes 15** minutes + cooling + **2** hours chilling | **3½ *POINTS*** values per recipe | **92** calories per serving

1 orange
11.5 g sachet **sugar free strawberry jelly**
200 ml (7 fl oz) boiling water
200 g pot **low fat strawberry yogurt**
1 heaped teaspoon caster sugar
1 teaspoon very finely chopped fresh **mint**
125 g (4½ oz) **strawberries***, diced*
1 **peach** *or* **nectarine***, stoned and diced*

Method

1 Finely grate ½ a teaspoon of zest from the orange and reserve for the salsa. Squeeze the juice from the orange into a bowl.

2 Pour the boiling water into a measuring jug and sprinkle on the jelly crystals. Stir to dissolve then add half the orange juice. Make up to 400 ml (14 fl oz) with cold water. Pour into a mixing bowl and leave to cool until room temperature, stirring occasionally.

3 Gradually stir the yogurt into the jelly liquid then divide between four mini pudding basins or ramekins. Cover and chill for 2 hours.

4 About 15 minutes before serving the castles, make the salsa. Crush the sugar, mint and orange zest together then mix with the rest of the orange juice, the strawberries and peach or nectarine.

5 Carefully unmould the castles, dipping the containers into hot water very briefly if necessary. Serve with the fruity salsa spooned on top.

Smart ideas...

Relax when you eat – even if it's just a snack. Not only does it prolong the pleasure, it helps digestion too. Try putting down your fork or spoon after each mouthful and see what a difference it makes.

1
POINTS
VALUE

Pear and ginger strudels

4 *POINTS* value

Serve with 150 ml (5 fl oz) low fat custard per person, for an additional 2 *POINTS* values per serving.

Serves 2 | **Takes 10** minutes to prepare, **15** minutes to cook | **8 *POINTS*** values per recipe | **228** calories per serving

411 g can **pear halves in natural juice***, drained*
2 pieces stem ginger in syrup, diced, plus 2 teaspoons syrup from the jar
2 x 45 g (1½ oz) frozen filo sheets, defrosted
2 teaspoons low fat spread, melted
low fat cooking spray
½ teaspoon icing sugar

Method

1 Preheat the oven to Gas Mark 6/200°C/fan oven 180°C. Roughly chop the pears then pat dry on kitchen paper. Mix with the diced ginger and ginger syrup.

2 Brush both sheets of filo lightly with the melted low fat spread then fold each one in half to make a square. Spoon half of the pear mixture along the top edge of each filo square, leaving 5 cm (2 inches) of pastry free at either end. Fold in the sides of the strudel then roll up, enclosing the filling.

3 Place the strudels on a baking tray sprayed with the cooking spray and bake for 15 minutes until crisp and golden. Dust with icing sugar just before serving.

Rhubarb and apple sponge pudding

4 *POINTS* value

A variation on Eve's pudding, this is at its best made with the forced pink rhubarb that appears in the shops in January. There's a lovely contrast between the hot fruity sponge and the cool vanilla yogurt.

Serves 6 | **Takes 10** minutes to prepare, **45** minutes to cook | **25½ *POINTS*** values per recipe | **291** calories per serving

2 cooking **apples***, peeled, cored and sliced*
250 g (9 oz) **rhubarb***, cut into 2.5 cm (1 inch) chunks*
150 g (5½ oz) caster sugar
125 g (4½ oz) self raising flour, sifted
50 g (1¾ oz) low fat spread
2 **eggs**
2 x 200 g pots **low fat vanilla yogurt**

Method

1 Preheat the oven to Gas Mark 4/180°C/fan oven 160°C. Place the sliced apples and rhubarb in a 23 cm (9 inch) ovenproof baking dish and scatter on 50 g (1¾ oz) caster sugar.

2 Add 3 tablespoons of water to the dish, cover with foil and bake for 20 minutes until the fruit is just tender.

3 After about 15 minutes, make the sponge by whisking together the rest of the sugar, flour, low fat spread, eggs and 50 g (1¾ oz) of the vanilla yogurt. Beat for 2 minutes until the sponge is pale and fluffy. Spoon the sponge mixture over the fruit and bake for 20–25 minutes until risen and golden brown.

4 Serve the pudding with the rest of the yogurt.

4
POINTS
VALUE

Fig and raspberry clafoutis

2 *POINTS* VALUE

3

A clafoutis is a French recipe for a light and sweet batter pudding. Traditionally made with prunes, this fresh fruit version uses raspberries and figs instead.

Ⓥ **Serves 6** | **Takes 10** minutes to prepare, **35** minutes to cook + **20** minutes resting | **11½** ***POINTS*** values per recipe | **134** calories per serving

low fat cooking spray
125 g (4½ oz) **raspberries**
4 fresh **figs***, trimmed and quartered*
2 **eggs**
50 g (1¾ oz) caster sugar
50 g (1¾ oz) plain flour
a pinch of salt
425 ml (15 fl oz) **skimmed milk**
1 teaspoon vanilla extract
½ teaspoon icing sugar

Method

1 Preheat the oven to Gas Mark 5/190°C/fan oven 170°C and place a baking sheet in the oven to preheat. Lightly spray a 23 cm (9 inch) ovenproof baking dish with the cooking spray and scatter in the raspberries and figs.

2 Whisk the eggs and sugar together in a large mixing bowl for about 3 minutes until pale, frothy and roughly doubled in volume. Sift in the flour and a pinch of salt then beat until smooth. Whisk in the milk and vanilla and pour the batter over the fruit in the dish.

3 Bake on the preheated baking sheet for 30–35 minutes until puffy and golden. Leave to rest for 20 minutes, as the pudding is better served warm rather than hot. Dust with icing sugar just before serving.

Ⓥ **Why not try...** making a store cupboard version of this recipe by replacing the fresh figs and raspberries with a 411 g can of apricot halves in natural juice, drained and patted dry on kitchen paper, for the same ***POINTS*** values per serving.

2
POINTS
VALUE

Pimms summer pudding

3½ POINTS VALUE

Serve with a tablespoon of very low fat fromage frais, for an extra ½ ***POINTS*** value.

Serves 4 | **Takes 15** minutes + **4** hours chilling | **14 *POINTS*** values per recipe | **209** calories per serving

500 g (1 lb 2 oz) **frozen summer fruits**
50 g (1¾ oz) caster sugar
50 ml (2 fl oz) Pimms (see Cook's tip)
7 medium slices bread, crusts removed

Method

1 Place the frozen fruits in a lidded saucepan with the caster sugar and 100 ml (3½ fl oz) water. Cover and cook for about 5 minutes or until the fruits have defrosted and are nice and juicy. Remove from the heat and stir in the Pimms.
2 Tip the fruit into a colander set over a bowl and drain for a couple of minutes then sit the colander back on top of the pan.
3 Cut the bread into pieces to fit four mini pudding basins, reserving enough bread to act as 'lids'. Dip the bread into the warm fruit juice and use to line the pudding basins. Spoon the fruits into the basins and top with the reserved bread 'lids', again dipped in the fruit juice. Cover the summer puddings with clingfilm, place on a plate and chill for at least 4 hours or overnight. Strain and reserve any leftover fruit juice.
4 Unmould the summer puddings and spoon over the reserved fruit juice to glaze.

Cook's tip... If you don't have any Pimms available, simply use a total of 150 ml (5 fl oz) water instead, for 2½ ***POINTS*** values per serving.

Hot chocolate pudding

4 POINTS VALUE

Luscious chocolate sponge in a pool of hot chocolate sauce – what more could you ask for?

Serves 6 | **Takes 10** minutes to prepare, **30** minutes to cook + cooling | **24 *POINTS*** values per recipe | **248** calories per serving

low fat cooking spray
40 g (1½ oz) cocoa, sifted
175 g (6 oz) soft dark brown sugar
125 g (4½ oz) self raising flour, sifted
60 g (2 oz) low fat spread, melted
175 ml (6 fl oz) **skimmed milk**
300 ml (10 fl oz) boiling water

Method

1 Preheat the oven to Gas Mark 4/180°C/fan oven 160°C and spray a 23 cm (9 inch) baking dish with the cooking spray.
2 In a mixing bowl, stir together half the cocoa with 125 g (4½ oz) of the sugar and the flour. Add the melted low fat spread and milk. Stir to mix well then scrape into the baking dish.
3 Mix the rest of the cocoa and sugar with the boiling water and pour this all over the sponge mixture in the dish. Bake for 30 minutes, during which time the pudding will separate into a light sponge on top of a chocolate sauce. Cool for 5 minutes or so before serving.

4
POINTS
VALUE

Chocolate orange brownies

These brownies have a fabulously fudgy texture – the secret is to make sure you don't over-bake them and then chill them before eating.

Makes 15 brownies | **Takes 10** minutes to prepare, **15** minutes to cook + **1** hour chilling | **25 *POINTS*** values per recipe | **101** calories per brownie

low fat cooking spray
175 g (6 oz) self raising flour
40 g (1½ oz) cocoa, reserving ½ a teaspoon for dusting
100 g (3½ oz) soft dark brown sugar
finely grated zest of an orange
1 **egg**
100 g (3½ oz) **very low fat natural yogurt**
75 g (2¾ oz) low fat spread, melted

Method

1 Preheat the oven to Gas Mark 4/180°C/fan oven 160°C. Line a 17 x 25 cm (6½ x 10 inch) rectangular cake tin with non stick baking parchment and spray with the cooking spray.

2 Sift the flour and cocoa into a mixing bowl then stir in the sugar and orange zest.

3 In a small bowl, beat the egg with the yogurt and 150 ml (5 fl oz) cold water then mix into the dry ingredients, followed by the low fat spread. Stir until smooth then pour into the prepared tin.

4 Bake for 15 minutes until just firm then cool in the tin. Once cool, chill in the fridge for at least 1 hour before cutting into 15 squares.

5 To serve, dust the reserved cocoa over the brownies.

Smart ideas...

When baking, use eggs at room temperature. They will whisk better, incorporating more air and giving a lighter result to your baked goods.

1 1/2
POINTS
VALUE

Festive fruity filo triangles

These taste just like mince pies, but you can enjoy them for fewer *POINTS* values. To enjoy them at their best, serve warm.

Makes 12 triangles | **Takes 15** minutes to prepare, **10** minutes to cook | **11½ *POINTS*** values per recipe | **61** calories per triangle

low fat cooking spray
1 orange
125 g (4½ oz) dried mixed fruit
1 teaspoon mixed spice
1 tablespoon brandy
150 g (5½ oz) **apple sauce**
2 x 45 g (1½ oz) frozen filo sheets, defrosted
½ teaspoon icing sugar

Method

1 Preheat the oven to Gas Mark 6/200°C/fan oven 180°C and spray a baking tray with the cooking spray. Finely grate 1 teaspoon of zest from the orange. Juice the orange and pour the juice into a lidded, non stick saucepan. Add the orange zest, the dried mixed fruit and the mixed spice. Cover and bring to a simmer then cook for 1–2 minutes until the dried fruit has plumped up and absorbed the juice.

2 Remove from the heat and stir in the brandy and the apple sauce. Set aside, covered, for 5 minutes.

3 Lay out the sheets of filo horizontally on a work surface and cut each one into six vertical strips to make 12 in total. Spray with the cooking spray.

4 Place 1 tablespoon of the filling at the top of each strip and then fold over and over in a triangular shape. Place on the baking tray. There is no need to spray the triangle tops.

5 Bake in the oven for 10 minutes until crisp and golden. Serve warm, dusted with the icing sugar.

1
POINTS
VALUE

Sticky orange buns

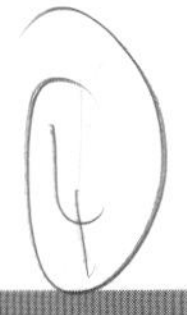

A fresh orange and honey glaze is brushed over these fragrant citrus-flavoured buns to give them an attractive glossy finish.

Makes 12 buns | **Takes 10** minutes to prepare, **15** minutes to cook | **25½ *POINTS*** values per recipe | **141** calories per bun

125 g (4½ oz) self raising flour
100 g (3½ oz) caster sugar
100 g (3½ oz) low fat spread
2 eggs
finely grated zest and juice of an orange
4 tablespoons clear honey

Method

1 Preheat the oven to Gas Mark 4/180°C/fan oven 160°C and line a 12 hole bun tin with paper cases.

2 Sift the flour into a mixing bowl. Add the sugar, low fat spread, eggs and orange zest. Beat together for 2 minutes using an electric whisk until pale and fluffy. Divide between the paper cases. Bake in the oven for 12–15 minutes until risen and golden.

3 While the buns are cooking, add the orange juice and honey to a small saucepan and boil for 5 minutes until reduced by about one third.

4 Remove the buns from the oven and brush the glaze over them while they are still warm then leave to cool.

Smart ideas...

When squeezing the juice from citrus fruits, you'll get more out of them if they aren't fridge cold. If necessary, heat them in the microwave on High for 10–15 seconds before juicing.

2
POINTS
VALUE

Lemon and passion fruit drizzle cake

2½ POINTS VALUE

Fragrant passion fruit combine beautifully with lemon in the topping for this delicious cake. Serve as a tea time treat or as a dessert, with a 50 g (1¾ oz) serving of fresh berries per person, for an extra ½ *POINTS* value per serving.

Serves 8 | **Takes 10** minutes to prepare, **25** minutes to cook + cooling | **21½ *POINTS*** values per recipe | **175** calories per serving

low fat cooking spray
100 g (3½ oz) self raising flour
1 teaspoon baking powder
125 g (4½ oz) caster sugar
75 g (2¾ oz) low fat spread
150 g (5½ oz) **apple sauce**
2 **eggs***, separated*
finely grated zest and juice of a lemon
2 **passion fruit***, halved*

Method

1 Preheat the oven to Gas Mark 4/180°C/fan oven 160°C. Line an 18 cm (7 inch) round cake tin with non stick baking parchment and spray with the cooking spray.

2 Sift the flour and baking powder into a mixing bowl and add 100 g (3½ oz) of the caster sugar, the low fat spread, apple sauce, egg yolks and lemon zest. Beat together for 2–3 minutes with an electric whisk until pale and fluffy.

3 Clean the whisk, then in a separate, clean bowl beat the egg whites to soft peaks. Gently fold into the cake mixture. Pour into the cake tin and level the surface. Bake for about 25 minutes or until risen, and firm in the centre.

4 Remove from the oven and place the tin on a cooling rack. Squeeze the passion fruit seeds and pulp into a bowl and mix with the lemon juice and the rest of the caster sugar. Prick the top of the cake with a skewer or fork and pour the lemon and passion fruit drizzle all over. Cool for 15 minutes then remove from the tin and place on the rack to finish cooling.

2 1/2
POINTS
VALUE

Coffee and walnut sponge

A truly delectable low *POINTS* value version of an all-time favourite recipe. Instead of the traditional buttercream filling, a delicious, sweet coffee icing is used instead.

Serves 8 | **Takes 20** minutes to prepare, **15** minutes to cook + cooling | **30 *POINTS*** values per recipe | **234** calories per serving

low fat cooking spray
150 g (5½ oz) self raising flour
1 teaspoon baking powder
100 g (3½ oz) caster sugar
2 **eggs**
100 g (3½ oz) low fat spread
75 g (2¾ oz) **low fat natural yogurt**
1 tablespoon instant coffee, dissolved in
1 tablespoon boiling water
25 g (1 oz) walnuts, chopped finely

For the icing
100 g (3½ oz) **low fat soft cheese**
2 tablespoons icing sugar, sifted
1 teaspoon instant coffee dissolved in
1 teaspoon boiling water

Method

1 Preheat the oven to Gas Mark 4/180°C/fan oven 160°C. Line two 18 cm (7 inch) round cake tins with non stick baking parchment and spray with the cooking spray.

2 Sift the flour and baking powder into a mixing bowl and add the sugar, eggs, low fat spread, yogurt and dissolved coffee. Beat for 2 minutes using an electric whisk until pale and fluffy. Stir in 15 g (½ oz) of the chopped walnuts then divide the cake mixture between the two tins. Level the surface then bake on the centre shelf for 15 minutes until risen and firm in the centre.

3 Cool in the tins for 5 minutes then remove and cool on a wire rack.

4 Meanwhile, make the icing. Stir the soft cheese and icing sugar together then mix in the dissolved coffee. Chill until needed.

5 When the cakes are completely cool, place one on a plate domed side down and spread with half the icing. Sit the other cake on top, dome side up, and spread with the remaining icing. Scatter with the rest of the chopped walnuts and cut into wedges to serve.

4
POINTS
VALUE

Crispy chocolate moments

These crunchy biscuits live up to their name and are a delicious way to savour a moment of chocolate.

Ⓥ **Makes 24** biscuits | **Takes 15** minutes to prepare, **10** minutes to cook + cooling | **20 *POINTS*** values per recipe | **54** calories per biscuit

low fat cooking spray
75 g (2¾ oz) low fat spread
75 g (2¾ oz) caster sugar
1 **egg** *yolk, beaten*
100 g (3½ oz) self raising flour
2 tablespoons cocoa
25 g (1 oz) cornflour
25 g (1 oz) **crisp rice cereal** *e.g.* **Rice Krispies**

Method

1 Preheat the oven to Gas Mark 4/180°C/fan oven 160°C. Spray two non stick baking trays with cooking spray and set aside.

2 In a large bowl, cream the low fat spread and sugar together using an electric whisk for 1 or 2 minutes until pale and fluffy then beat in the egg yolk.

3 Sift in the flour, cocoa and cornflour and combine using a wooden spoon. Dampen your hands so that the mixture won't stick, then roll into 24 truffle sized balls.

4 Roll the balls in the crisp rice cereal to coat then place, spaced out, on the two baking trays. Press each one down to flatten. Bake for 10 minutes until set.

5 Remove the baking trays from the oven and cool on the trays for 5 minutes to firm up then transfer to a wire rack to cool completely. Store in an airtight container for up to 1 week.

Smart ideas...

Use good quality cocoa powder for baking to enjoy an intensely rich chocolate flavour. Never use drinking chocolate powder instead; it simply won't deliver on flavour due to a much lower cocoa content.

1
POINTS
VALUE

Breakfast

Lunches and light bites

Midweek meals in minutes

Cooking for one

Vegetarian

Family favourites

Comfort food

Celebrate

Something on the side

Desserts and bakes